TRIUMPHANT SERVICE SONGS

AN ALL PURPOSE BOOK PREPARED TO MEET THE REQUIREMENTS OF EVERY DEPARTMENT OF CHURCH WORK

~~~

Compiled By

HOMER A. RODEHEAVER   YUMBERT P. RODEHEAVER
GEORGE W. SANVILLE   JOSEPH N. RODEHEAVER

~~~

Full Cloth, Board
Brown Bristol Paper

~~~

ORCHESTRATIONS

1. Solo Violin (or Flute)
2. First Violin (or C Melody Saxophone)
3. Second Violin
4. Cello and Bass
5. First B♭ Clarinet
6. Second B♭ Clarinet
7. E♭ Alto Saxophone
8. E♭ Alto Horns
9. Cornets (1st and 2nd)
10. Trombone (Treble)
11. Trombone (Bass)
12. Piano

~~~

PUBLISHED BY

The RODEHEAVER Co.
HALL-MACK
WINONA LAKE, INDIANA

PRINTED IN THE U.S.A.

Copyright 1934 by Homer Rodeheaver

Order of Worship

Voluntary, instrumental or vocal.

Singing from the Hymnal, the people standing.

The Apostles' Creed, recited by all, still standing.

I believe in God the Father Almighty, Maker of heaven and earth; and in Jesus Christ His only Son our Lord; who was conceived by the Holy Ghost, born of the Virgin Mary, suffered under Pontius Pilate, was crucified, dead, and buried; the third day he rose again from the dead, he ascended into heaven, and sitteth at the right hand of God the Father Almighty; from thence he shall come to judge the quick and the dead I believe in the Holy Ghost; the holy catholic Church, the communion of saints; the forgiveness of sins; the resurrection of the body; and the life everlasting. Amen.

Prayer, concluding with the Lord's Prayer, re peated audibly by all.

Anthem, or **Voluntary.**

Lesson from the Old Testament, which, if from the Psalms, may be read responsively.

The Gloria Patri.

Glory be to the Father, and to the Son, and to the Holy Ghost; as it was in the beginning, is now, and ever shall be, world without end. Amen.]

Lesson from the New Testament.

Notices, followed by collection; during which or after which an offertory may be rendered.

Singing from the Hymnal, the people standing.

The Sermon.

Prayer.

Singing from the Hymnal, the people standing.*

Doxology and the Apostolic Benediction.

*An invitation to come to Christ, or to unite with the Church, should be given when this hymn is announced.

INVOCATION SENTENCE

In Unison or Harmony   Karl P. Harrington

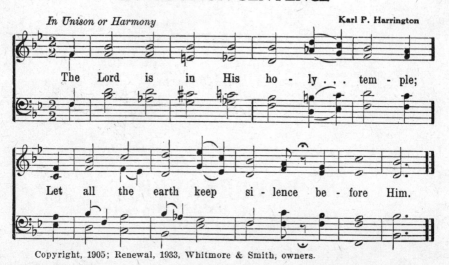

The Lord is in His ho - ly . . . tem - ple;

Let all the earth keep si - lence be - fore Him.

Copyright, 1905; Renewal, 1933, Whitmore & Smith, owners.

TRIUMPHANT SERVICE SONGS

1   O WORSHIP THE KING

Sir Robert Grant

Francis Joseph Haydn

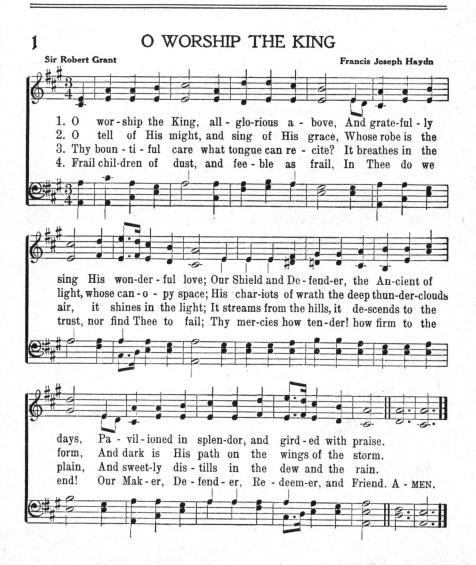

1. O wor-ship the King, all-glo-rious a-bove, And grate-ful-ly
2. O tell of His might, and sing of His grace, Whose robe is the
3. Thy boun-ti-ful care what tongue can re-cite? It breathes in the
4. Frail chil-dren of dust, and fee-ble as frail, In Thee do we

sing His won-der-ful love; Our Shield and De-fend-er, the An-cient of
light, whose can-o-py space; His char-iots of wrath the deep thun-der-clouds
air, it shines in the light; It streams from the hills, it de-scends to the
trust, nor find Thee to fail; Thy mer-cies how ten-der! how firm to the

days, Pa-vil-ioned in splen-dor, and gird-ed with praise.
form, And dark is His path on the wings of the storm.
plain, And sweet-ly dis-tills in the dew and the rain.
end! Our Mak-er, De-fend-er, Re-deem-er, and Friend. A-MEN.

2   JESUS TOOK MY BURDEN

Rev. Johnson Oatman Jr.   Bertha Mae Lillenas

1. When I, a poor, lost sin-ner, Be-fore the Lord did fall, And in the name of
2. Oft-times the way is drear-y, And rugged seems the road, Oft-times I'm weak and
3. When I was crushed with sorrow I bowed in deep de-spair, My load of grief and
4. I'll trust Him for the fu-ture, He know-eth all the way, For with His eye He'll

Je - sus For par-don loud did call; He heard my sup-pli-ca-tion, And
wea - ry, When bent beneath some load; But when I cry in weak-ness, "How
heart-ache Seemed more than I could bear; 'Twas then I heard a whis-per, "You
guide me A - long life's pil-grim way; And I will tell in heav-en, While

soon the weak was strong, For Je-sus took my bur-den, And left me with a song.
long, O Lord, how long?" Then Je-sus takes the bur-den, And leaves me with a song.
to the Lord be-long," Then Je-sus took my bur-den, And left me with a song.
a - ges roll a - long, How Je-sus took my bur-den, And left me with a song.

CHORUS

Yes, Je - sus took my bur-den I could no lon-ger bear, Yes, Je-sus took my

bur-den In an-swer to my prayer; My anx-ious fears sub-sid-ed My

JESUS TOOK MY BURDEN

spir-it was made strong, For Je-sus took my bur-den, And left me with a song.

3

HE LIFTED ME

Charlotte G. Homer

Chas. H. Gabriel

1. In   lov-ing kind-ness Je-sus came, My soul in mer - cy to re-claim,
2. He called me long be - fore I heard, Be-fore my sin-ful heart was stirred,
3. His brow was pierced with man-y a thorn, His hands by cru - el nails were torn,
4. Now on a high-er plane I dwell, And with my soul I know 'tis well;

And from the depths of sin and shame Thro' grace He lift - ed me........
But when I took Him at His word, For-giv'n He lift - ed me........
When from my guilt and grief, for-lorn, In   love He lift - ed me........
Yet how or why, I can-not tell, He should have lift - ed me........
He lift-ed me.

CHORUS

From sink-ing sand He lift - ed me, With ten-der hand He lift - ed me,

From shades of night to planes of light, O praise His name, He lift-ed me!

4 MY FAITH LOOKS UP TO THEE

RAY PALMER

LOWELL MASON

1. My faith looks up to Thee, Thou Lamb of Cal - va - ry, Sav - ior di - vine; Now hear me
2. May Thy rich grace impart Strength to my fainting heart, My zeal in - spire; As Thou hast
3. While life's dark maze I tread, And griefs around me spread, Be Thou my Guide; Bid darkness

when I pray, Take all my sin a - way, O let me from this day Be whol - ly Thine!
died for me, O may my love to Thee, Pure, warm, and changeless be,—A liv - ing fire!
turn to day, Wipe sorrow's tears a - way, Nor let me ev - er stray From Thee a - side.

5 MY JESUS, I LOVE THEE

ANONYMOUS

A. J. GORDON

1. My Je - sus, I love Thee, I know Thou art mine, For Thee all the
2. I'll love Thee in life, I will love Thee in death, And praise Thee as
3. In mansions of glo - ry and end - less de - light, I'll ev - er a -

pleas - ures of sin I re - sign; My gra - cious Re - deem - er, my
long as Thou lend - est me breath; And say when the death-dew lies
dore Thee in heav - en so bright; I'll sing with the glit - ter - ing

Sav - ior art Thou; If ev - er I loved Thee, my Je - sus, 'tis now.
cold on my brow, If ev - er I loved Thee, my Je - sus, 'tis now.
crown on my brow, If ev - er I loved Thee, my Je - sus, 'tis now.

6

LET US BE JOYFUL

T. O. Chisholm　　　　　　　　　　　　　　　　　　　　**Jesse B. Thomas**

1. Let us be joy - ful, we that are Chris - tian, Lift heart and
2. Once we were al - iens, now we are chil - dren, Once, grop - ing
3. Won-drous the gifts and boun-teous the bless - ings. Which we as
4. Let us be joy - ful, sing ing to - geth - er Hymns of thanks-

voice in ju - bi-lant song; So man - y rea - sons have we for glad-ness,
blind - ly, now we can see; "All we like sheep" were help-less-ly stray-ing,
heirs of grace have re - ceived; Life more a - bun-dant, peace like a riv - er,
giv - ing, an-thems of praise; With songs of rap-ture, psalms of de - vo-tion,

CHORUS

We should be sing - ing all the day long.
Now in the fold of the Shepherd are we.　　　**Let us re-joice with ju - bi-lant**
Love pass-ing knowl-edge, since we be - lieved.
Ring-ing ho - san - nas, fill - ing our days.

sing - ing O - ver the treas - ures re-vealed in His Word, Sing of the

love of Christ who redeemed us, Singing with grace in our hearts to the Lord.

7   I AM PRAYING FOR YOU

S. O'Maley Cluff

Ira D. Sankey

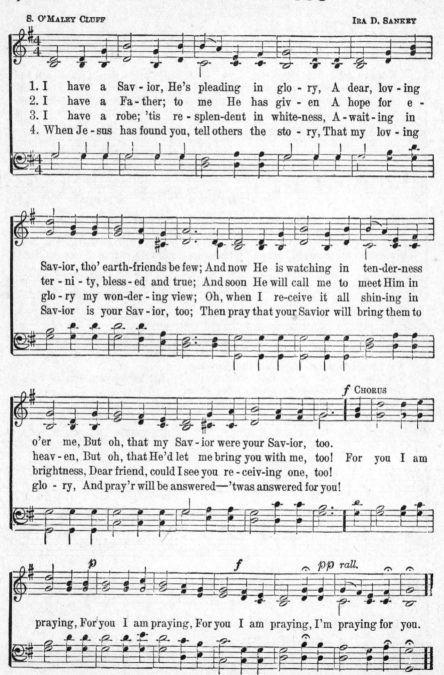

1. I have a Sav - ior, He's pleading in glo - ry, A dear, lov - ing
2. I have a Fa - ther; to me He has giv - en A hope for e -
3. I have a robe; 'tis re - splen-dent in white-ness, A - wait-ing in
4. When Je - sus has found you, tell others the sto - ry, That my lov - ing

Sav-ior, tho' earth-friends be few; And now He is watching in ten-der-ness
ter - ni - ty, bless - ed and true; And soon He will call me to meet Him in
glo - ry my won-der - ing view; Oh, when I re-ceive it all shin-ing in
Sav-ior is your Sav - ior, too; Then pray that your Savior will bring them to

o'er me, But oh, that my Sav - ior were your Sav-ior, too.
heav - en, But oh, that He'd let me bring you with me, too! For you I am
brightness, Dear friend, could I see you re - ceiv-ing one, too!
glo - ry, And pray'r will be answered—'twas answered for you!

praying, For you I am praying, For you I am praying, I'm praying for you.

8 YOU MUST OPEN THE DOOR

Ina Duley Ogdon

COPYRIGHT, 1934, BY HOMER A. RODEHEAVER
INTERNATIONAL COPYRIGHT SECURED

Homer A. Rodeheaver

1. There's a Sav-ior who stands at the door of your heart, He is
2. He has come from the Fa-ther sal-va-tion to bring, And His
3. He is lov-ing and kind, full of in-fi-nite grace, In your
4. He will lead you at last to that bless-ed a-bode, To the

long-ing to en-ter—why let Him de-part? He has pa-tient-ly
name is called Je-sus, Re-deem-er and King; To save you and
heart, in your life, will you give Him a place? He is wait-ing to
cit-y of God, at the end of the road, Where the night nev-er

called you so oft-en be-fore, But you must o-pen the door.
keep you He pleads ev-er-more, But you must o-pen the door.
bless you, your soul to re-store, But you must o-pen the door.
falls, when life's jour-ney is o'er, But you must o-pen the door.

CHORUS

You must o-pen the door, You must o-pen the door, When

Je-sus comes in, He will save you from sin, But you must o-pen the door.

9   LOVE DIVINE

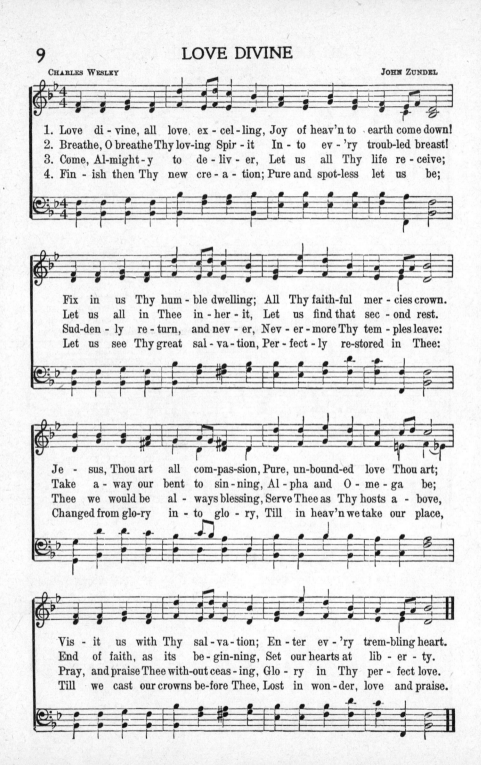

CHARLES WESLEY

JOHN ZUNDEL

1. Love di - vine, all love. ex - cel - ling, Joy of heav'n to earth come down!
2. Breathe, O breathe Thy lov-ing Spir - it In - to ev - 'ry troub-led breast!
3. Come, Al-might - y to de - liv - er, Let us all Thy life re - ceive;
4. Fin - ish then Thy new cre - a - tion; Pure and spot-less let us be;

Fix in us Thy hum - ble dwelling; All Thy faith-ful mer - cies crown.
Let us all in Thee in - her - it, Let us find that sec - ond rest.
Sud-den - ly re - turn, and nev - er, Nev - er - more Thy tem - ples leave:
Let us see Thy great sal - va - tion, Per - fect - ly re-stored in Thee:

Je - sus, Thou art all com-pas-sion, Pure, un-bound-ed love Thou art;
Take a - way our bent to sin - ning, Al - pha and O - me - ga be;
Thee we would be al - ways blessing, Serve Thee as Thy hosts a - bove,
Changed from glo-ry in - to glo - ry, Till in heav'n we take our place,

Vis - it us with Thy sal - va - tion; En - ter ev - 'ry trem-bling heart.
End of faith, as its be - gin-ning, Set our hearts at lib - er - ty.
Pray, and praise Thee with-out ceas - ing, Glo - ry in Thy per - fect love.
Till we cast our crowns be-fore Thee, Lost in won - der, love and praise.

10   A REVIVAL HYMN

Rev. Oswald J. Smith

B. D. Ackley

1. Re - vive Thy work, O Lord! And man - i - fest Thy pow'r;
2. Re - vive Thy work, O Lord! And ev - 'ry soul in - spire;
3. Re - vive Thy work, O Lord! And give a-bound-ing joy;
4. Re - vive Thy work, O Lord! And make Thy serv-ants bold;
5. Re - vive Thy work, O Lord! Ful - fill Thy prom-ise true;

Thy work, O Lord!

O come up - on Thy church, and give A pen - i - ten - tial show'r!
O kin - dle in each heart, we pray, The pen - te - cos - tal fire!
O fill our hearts with per - fect love, And burn out all al - loy!
Con - vict of sin, and work once more As in the days of old.
Let Je - sus Christ be glo - ri - fied, And great things for us do.

CHORUS

Re - vive Thy work, O Lord, Come now and an - swer prayer;

an-swer prayer;

O come in Ho - ly Spir - it pow'r, And save men ev - 'ry - where.

TELL IT OUT

Rev. A. H. Ackley

B. D. Ackley

1. Is the Christ that you worship now liv-ing or dead? Tell it out, ...
2. Have you found the redemption from sin thro' the cross?
3. Is there hope when the fu-ture seems dark with despair?
4. Do you want to help oth-ers find life thro' His name? Tell it out,

tell it out! . . . . If you know it and feel it then let it be said,
Have you found Christ the gain that makes up for all loss?
Do you know from experience that Christ will be there?
tell it out! Would you seek to es - tab-lish the truth of His claim?

Chorus

Tell it out, ... tell it out! . . . . Tell it out, tell it out, till the
Tell it out, tell it out!

Slower

whole world shall know, You have found the great joy only Christ can bestow; They are

a tempo

waiting to hear it wher-ev-er you go, Tell it out, ... tell it out! . . . .
Tell it out, tell it out!

BLESSED ASSURANCE

FANNY J. CROSBY

MRS. JOS. F. KNAPP

1. Bless-ed as-sur-ance, Je-sus is mine! O what a fore-taste of
2. Per-fect sub-mis-sion, per-fect de-light, Vi-sions of rap-ture now
3. Per-fect sub-mis-sion, all is at rest, I in my Sav-ior am

glo-ry di-vine! Heir of sal-va-tion, purchase of God, Born of His
burst on my sight! Angels de-scend-ing, bring from a-bove Ech-oes of
hap-py and blest; Watching and waiting, look-ing a-bove, Filled with His

Spir-it, washed in His blood.
mer-cy, whis-pers of love.
good-ness, lost in His love.

CHORUS

This is my sto-ry, this is my song, Prais-ing my Sav-ior all the day long; This is my sto-ry, this is my song, Praising my Sav-ior all the day long.

I LOVE TO TELL THE STORY

KATHERINE HANKEY

WILLIAM G. FISCHER

1. I love to tell the sto - ry Of un - seen things a - bove, Of Je - sus
2. I love to tell the sto - ry; More won-der - ful it seems Than all the
3. I love to tell the sto - ry; 'Tis pleas-ant to re - peat What seems each
4. I love to tell the sto - ry; For those who know it best Seem hun - ger-

and His glo - ry, Of Je - sus and His love, I love to tell the sto - ry,
gold - en fan-cies Of all my golden dreams. I love to tell the sto - ry
time I tell it, More won-der-ful - ly sweet. I love to tell the sto - ry;
ing and thirsting To hear it like the rest. And when, in scenes of glo - ry,

Because I know 'tis true, It sat - is-fies my longings, As nothing else can do.
It did so much for me; And that is just the rea-son I tell it now to thee
For some have never heard The message of salvation From God's own holy word.
I sing the new, new song, 'Twill be the old, old story, That I have loved so long.

CHORUS

I love to tell the sto - ry! 'Twill be my theme in glo - ry

To tell the old, old sto - ry Of Je - sus and His love.

14 CHIEFEST OF TEN THOUSAND

A. H. A.

Rev. A. H. Ackley

1. All the Sav-ior's glo-ry mind can nev-er meas-ure, Nor the tongue of
2. Mine in time of troub-le when my heart is break-ing, When my spir-it
3. He's my strength in weakness, joy in times of sad-ness, My pro-tec-tion
4. And in earth or heav-en there is not His e-qual, Saints nor an-gels

man de-fine (de-fine); I have come to know Him as life's dear-est treas-ure,
droops with grief (with grief), He with bless-ed com-fort heals the bit-ter ach-ing,
from the foe (the foe), Patient, kind and lov-ing, heart of all my glad-ness,
can com-pare (compare), Nor the matchless splendors of the realm su-per-nal,

Chorus

Know Him as my friend di-vine.
Swift and sure He brings relief. Fairer than the morning, brighter than the noonday,
He dis-pels my ev-'ry foe.
He's the fair-est of the fair.

Love-lier than the sun-set up-on the qui-et sea, Pur-er than the lil-y,

sweet-er than the bird's song, Chiefest of ten thousand is Je-sus Christ to me.

T. O. CHISHOLM
Not fast

C. HAROLD LOWDEN

1. Liv-ing for Je-sus a life that is true, Striving to please Him in all that I do,
2. Liv-ing for Je-sus who died in my place, Bearing on Calv'ry my sin and disgrace,
3. Liv-ing for Je-sus wher-ev-er I am, Do-ing each du-ty in His Ho-ly Name,
4. Living for Jesus thro' earth's little while, My dearest treasure, the light of His smile,

Yielding allegiance, glad-hearted and free, This is the pathway of blessing for me.
Such love constrains me to answer His call, Follow His leading and give Him my all.
Will-ing to suf-fer af-flic-tion or loss, Deeming each trial a part of my cross.
Seek-ing the lost ones He died to redeem, Bringing the weary to find rest in Him.

*CHORUS. UNISON. *A little slower.*

O Je-sus, Lord and Savior, I give my-self to Thee; For Thou, in Thy a -

tonement, Didst give Thyself for me; I own no oth-er Mas-ter, My

rit.............

heart shall be Thy throne, My life I give, henceforth to live. O Christ, for Thee alone.

*Melody in lower notes. A two-part effect may be had by having the men sing the melody, the women taking the middle notes.

16 WILLING TO TAKE THE CROSS

Floyd W. Hawkins

Floyd W. Hawkins

DUET

1. From His ce - les - tial a - bode Je - sus came, Will-ing to die for man;
2. O the deep shame Je-sus suf-fered that day, Bear-ing the sin - ful stain;
3. How could the Sav-ior, so spot-less and pure, Leave that bright home on high;
4. Come to the Sav-ior with all of thy guilt, Come with thy load of sin;

Tak - ing the cross with its suff'ring and shame, He laid re-demp-tion's plan.
Will-ing to suf - fer our ran-som to pay, Will-ing to bear the pain.
Will-ing the way of the cross to en - dure, Will-ing to bleed and die?
It was for thee that His life's blood was spilt, Je - sus will take you in.

CHORUS

Will-ing to take the cross was He, Will-ing to suf-fer mis - er - y, Will-ing to go to

Cal - va-ry, Laying His glo-ry a - side; Will-ing to hang there on the tree, Will-ing to

bear the ag - o - ny, Will-ing to die for you and me; Je-sus the Cru-ci - fied.

17 THIS IS MY FATHER'S WORLD

Maltbie D. Babcock   TERRA BEATA S. M. D.

Traditional English Melody
Arranged by S. F. L.

1. This is my Fa-ther's world, And to my list-'ning ears, All na-ture sings, and round me rings The mu-sic of the spheres. This is my Fa-ther's world, I rest me in the thought Of rocks and trees, of skies and seas—His hand the won-ders wrought.

2. This is my Fa-ther's world, The birds their car-ols raise, The morn-ing light, the lil-y white, De-clare their Ma-ker's praise. This is my Fa-ther's world, He shines in all that's fair; In the rus-tling grass I hear Him pass, He speaks to me ev-'ry-where.

3. This is my Fa-ther's world, Oh! let me ne'er for-get That though the wrong seems oft so strong, God is the Ru-ler yet. This is my Fa-ther's world, The bat-tle is not done, Je-sus who died shall be sat-is-fied, And earth and heav'n be one. A-men.

18   IT IS MORNING IN MY HEART

A. H. A.   Rev. A. H. Ackley.

1. All the dark-ness of the night has passed a-way, It is morn-ing in my
2. I can hear the songbirds sing-ing their re-frain, It is morn-ing in my
3. Christ has made the world a par-a-dise to me, It is morn-ing in my
4. Joy has come to dwell with me for-ev-er-more, It is morn-ing in my

heart; I am liv-ing in the sun-light of the day, It is
heart; And I know that life for me be-gins a-gain, It is
heart; Ev-'ry du-ty in the light of love I see, It is
heart, I shall sing it when I reach the oth-er shore, It is

REFRAIN

morn-ing in my heart. It is morning, it is morning in my heart, . . .
in my heart,

Je-sus made the gloomy shadows all de-part; . . . . . Songs of gladness now I
made all de-part;

sing, for since Je-sus is my King It is morning, it is morn-ing in my heart.

19   GRACE GREATER THAN OUR SIN

Julia H. Johnston.

D. B. Towner.

1. Mar - vel - ous grace of our lov - ing Lord, Grace that ex-ceeds our
2. Sin and de-spair like the sea waves cold, Threat-en the soul with
3. Dark is the stain that we can - not hide, What can a - vail to
4. Mar - vel - ous, in - fi - nite, match-less grace, Free - ly bestowed on

sin and our guilt, Yon - der on Cal - va - ry's mount out - poured,
in - fi - nite loss; Grace that is great - er, yes, grace un - told,
wash it a - way? Look, there is flow - ing a crim - son tide;
all who be - lieve; You that are long - ing to see His face,

CHORUS.

There where the blood of the Lamb was spilt. Grace, grace,
Points to the Ref - uge, the Might - y Cross.
Whit - er than snow you may be to - day.
Will you this mo - ment His grace re - ceive? Mar - vel - ous grace,

God's grace, Grace that will par-don and cleanse with-in; Grace
In - fi - nite grace,   Mar - vel - ous

grace, God's grace, Grace that is great-er than all our sin.
grace, In - fi - nite grace,

20 FOLLOW THE GLEAM

Silver Bay Prize Song
BRYN MAWR COLLEGE

Sallie Hume Douglas

1. To the Knights in the days of old, Keep-ing watch on the
2. And we who would serve the King And loy-al-ly

moun-tain height, Came a vi-sion of Ho-ly Grail And a
Him o-bey, In the con-se-crate si-lence know That the

voice thro' the wait-ing night, Fol-low, fol-low, fol-low the gleam,
challenge still holds to-day. Fol-low, fol-low, fol-low the gleam,

Ban-ners un-furled o'er all the world, Fol-low, fol-low,
Stand-ards of worth o'er all the earth, Fol-low, fol-low,

fol-low the gleam Of the Chal-ice that is the Grail.
fol-low the gleam Of the light that shall bring the dawn.

21   GUIDE ME, O THOU GREAT JEHOVAH

WILLIAM WILLIAMS   THOMAS HASTINGS

1. Guide me, O Thou great Je - ho - vah, Pil - grim thro' this bar - ren
2. O - pen now the crys - tal fount - ain Whence the heal - ing wa - ters
3. When I tread the verge of Jor - dan, Bid my anx - ious fears sub -

land; I am weak, but Thou art might - y, Hold me with Thy pow'r - ful
flow; Let the fi - er - y, cloud - y pil - lar Lead me all my jour - ney
side; Bear me thro' the swell - ing cur - rent, Land me safe on Ca - naan's

hand; Bread of heav - en, Feed me till I want no more;
thro'; Strong De - liv - 'rer, Be Thou still my Strength and Shield;
side: Songs of prais - es I will ev - er give to Thee;

Bread of heav - en, Feed me till I want no more.
Strong De - liv - 'rer, Be Thou still my Strength and Shield.
Songs of prais - es I will ev - er give to Thee.

22 THE PEACE THAT MY SAVIOR HAS GIVEN

H. L.

Haldor Lillenas

DUET *Slowly*

1. Like the fra-grance of flow-ers, Like the soft sum-mer show-ers, Is the
2. Like the twi-light comes stealing, Like an eve-ning bell peal-ing, Is the
3. Like a cloud that is rift-ed, Like a bur-den that's lift-ed, Is the

peace that my Sav-ior has giv - en; Like the dews of the morn-ing All the
peace that my Sav-ior has giv - en; Like a sun-set of splen-dor, Like a
peace that my Sav-ior has giv - en; Like a rest aft-er sor-row, Like a

rit.

hill-sides a-dorn-ing, Is the peace that my Sav-ior has giv - en.
song sweet and ten-der, Is the peace that my Sav-ior has giv - en.
ju - bi-lant mor-row, Is the peace that my Sav-ior has giv - en.

CHORUS *Parts*

Peace that my Savior has giv - en, Peace that He sendeth from heav - en; As
Peace that my Sav-ior has giv-en, Peace that He sendeth from heaven;

rit.

high as the mountain and deep as the sea Is the peace Jesus gives to me (gives to me).

ANONYMOUS

FELICE DE GIARDINI

1. Come, Thou Al - might - y King, Help us Thy name to sing,
2. Come, Thou In - car - nate Word, Gird on Thy might - y sword,
3. Come, Ho - ly Com - fort - er, Thy sa - cred wit - ness bear
4. To the great One in Three E - ter - nal prais - es be

Help us to praise: Fa - ther, all - glo - ri - ous, O'er all vic -
Our pray'r at - tend: Come, and Thy peo - ple bless, And give Thy
In this glad hour: Thou who al - might - y art, Now rule in
Hence ev - er - more. His sov - 'reign maj - es - ty May we in

to - ri - ous, Come, and reign o - ver us, An - cient of Days.
word suc - cess: Spir - it of ho - li - ness, On us de - scend.
ev - 'ry heart, And ne'er from us de - part, Spir - it of pow'r.
glo - ry see, And to e - ter - ni - ty, Love and a - dore.

24 RISE UP, O MEN OF GOD

William P. Merrill

William H. Walter

1. Rise up, O men of God! Have done with less - er things; Give
2. Rise up, O men of God! His king - dom tar - ries long: Bring
3. Rise up, O men of God! The Church for you doth wait, Her
4. Lift high the cross of Christ! Tread where His feet have trod: As

RISE UP, O MEN OF GOD

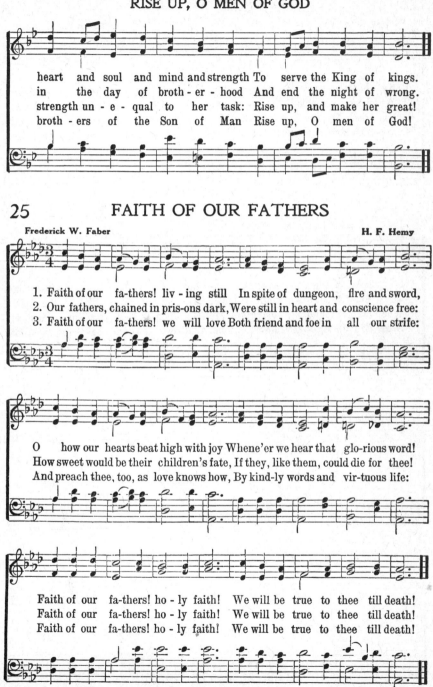

heart and soul and mind and strength To serve the King of kings.
in the day of broth - er - hood And end the night of wrong.
strength un - e - qual to her task: Rise up, and make her great!
broth - ers of the Son of Man Rise up, O men of God!

25 FAITH OF OUR FATHERS

Frederick W. Faber

H. F. Hemy

1. Faith of our fa-thers! liv - ing still In spite of dungeon, fire and sword,
2. Our fathers, chained in pris-ons dark, Were still in heart and conscience free:
3. Faith of our fa-thers! we will love Both friend and foe in all our strife:

O how our hearts beat high with joy Whene'er we hear that glo-rious word!
How sweet would be their children's fate, If they, like them, could die for thee!
And preach thee, too, as love knows how, By kind-ly words and vir-tuous life:

Faith of our fa-thers! ho - ly faith! We will be true to thee till death!
Faith of our fa-thers! ho - ly faith! We will be true to thee till death!
Faith of our fa-thers! ho - ly faith! We will be true to thee till death!

MY HOPE IS BUILT

EDWARD MOTE

WILLIAM B. BRADBURY

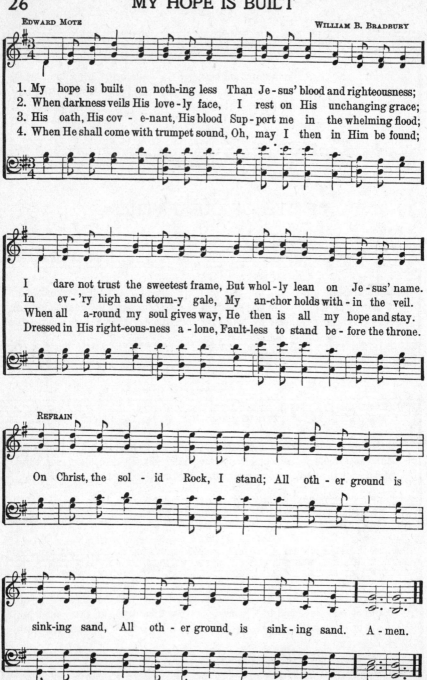

1. My hope is built on noth-ing less Than Je - sus' blood and righteousness;
2. When darkness veils His love - ly face, I rest on His unchanging grace;
3. His oath, His cov - e-nant, His blood Sup-port me in the whelming flood;
4. When He shall come with trumpet sound, Oh, may I then in Him be found;

I dare not trust the sweetest frame, But whol-ly lean on Je - sus' name.
In ev - 'ry high and storm-y gale, My an-chor holds with - in the veil.
When all a-round my soul gives way, He then is all my hope and stay.
Dressed in His right-eous-ness a - lone, Fault-less to stand be - fore the throne.

REFRAIN

On Christ, the sol - id Rock, I stand; All oth - er ground is

sink-ing sand, All oth - er ground is sink - ing sand. A - men.

THE MERCIES OF GOD

T. O. Chisholm   Jesse B. Thomas

1. The mer-cies of God! what a theme for my song, Oh! I nev-er could
2. They greet me at morn when I wak-en from sleep, And they glad-den my
3. His an-gels of mer-cy en-com-pass me 'round, Where-so-ev-er my
4. His good-ness and mer-cy will fol-low me still, E-ven on to the

num-ber them o'er; They're more than the stars in the heav-en-ly dome,
heart at the noon; They fol-low me on in-to shades of the night,
path-way may lead; Each turn of the road some new to-ken re-veals—
end of the way; I have His sure prom-ise and that can-not fail,

CHORUS

Or the sands of the wave-beat-en shore. For mer-cies so great, what re-
When the day with its la-bor is done.
Oh! for me life is bless-ed in-deed.
That His mer-cy en-dur-eth for aye.

turn can I make? For mer-cies so con-stant and sure? I'll love Him, I'll

serve Him with all that I have As long as my life shall en-dure.

THE SUN WILL SHINE AGAIN

A, H. A.   A. H. Ackley

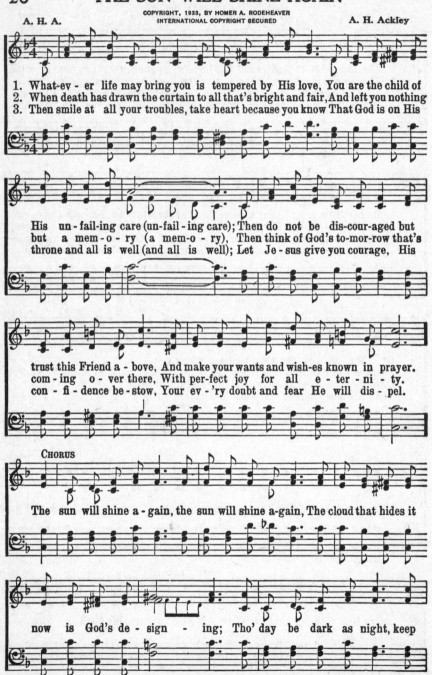

1. What-ev - er life may bring you is tempered by His love, You are the child of
2. When death has drawn the curtain to all that's bright and fair, And left you nothing
3. Then smile at all your troubles, take heart because you know That God is on His

His un - fail-ing care (un-fail - ing care); Then do not be dis-cour-aged but
but a mem-o - ry (a mem-o - ry), Then think of God's to-mor-row that's
throne and all is well (and all is well); Let Je - sus give you courage, His

trust this Friend a - bove, And make your wants and wish-es known in prayer.
com - ing o - ver there, With per-fect joy for all e - ter - ni - ty.
con - fi - dence be - stow, Your ev - 'ry doubt and fear He will dis - pel.

CHORUS

The sun will shine a - gain, the sun will shine a-gain, The cloud that hides it

now is God's de - sign - ing; Tho' day be dark as night, keep

THE SUN WILL SHINE AGAIN

look-ing for the light, For just be-hind the cloud the sun is shin - ing.

29   ALL THAT I NEED

W. C. Poole   J. M. Hagan

1. All that I need will God's grace sup-ply, All, all that I need;
2. All that I need is His prom-ise true, All, all that I need;
3. All that I need in the try - ing hour, All, all that I need;
4. All that I need when I reach life's end, All, all that I need;

All that I need and no good de - ny, God will give all that I need.
Strength for each day all His work to do, God will give all that I need.
All that I need of His grace and pow'r, God will give all that I need.
All that I need with my Sav-ior, Friend, God will give all that I need.

Chorus

All that I need with-out, with-in, All that I need to con-quer all sin,

All that I need to vic - to - ry win, God will give all that I need.

30 MY SAVIOR'S LOVE

C. H. G.

CHAS. H. GABRIEL

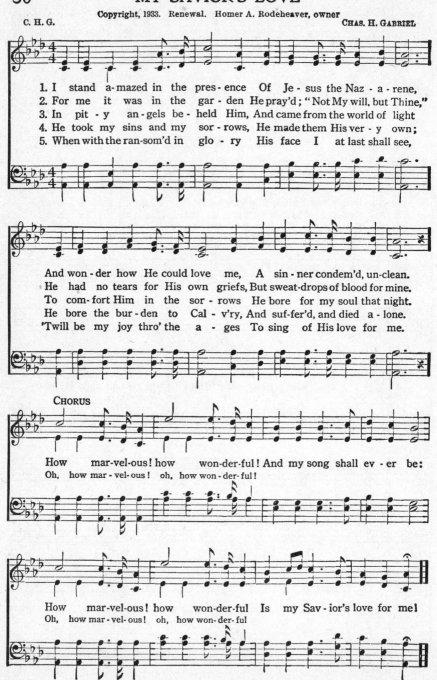

1. I stand a-mazed in the pres-ence Of Je-sus the Naz-a-rene,
2. For me it was in the gar-den He pray'd; "Not My will, but Thine,"
3. In pit-y an-gels be-held Him, And came from the world of light
4. He took my sins and my sor-rows, He made them His ver-y own;
5. When with the ran-som'd in glo-ry His face I at last shall see,

And won-der how He could love me, A sin-ner condem'd, un-clean.
He had no tears for His own griefs, But sweat-drops of blood for mine.
To com-fort Him in the sor-rows He bore for my soul that night.
He bore the bur-den to Cal-v'ry, And suf-fer'd, and died a-lone.
'Twill be my joy thro' the a-ges To sing of His love for me.

CHORUS

How mar-vel-ous! how won-der-ful! And my song shall ev-er be:
Oh, how mar-vel-ous! oh, how won-der-ful!

How mar-vel-ous! how won-der-ful Is my Sav-ior's love for me!
Oh, how mar-vel-ous! oh, how won-der-ful

31
ALL ALONE

Jno. R. Clements

B. D. Ackley

DUET

1. When my feet have been torn with the rough, ston-y way, And my heart it is sad at the end of the day; When my spir-it is troub-led till scarce I can see, I sit all a-lone with Je-sus.

2. When the world has passed by with no wel-com-ing smile; When my task takes me on to the sec-ond long mile, And the hard hand of sin my soul would de-file— I steal all a-lone to Je-sus.

3. When some friend has grown cold, thro' a fan-ci-ful wrong, And the hand li-eth weak that has al-ways been strong; When my voice shall be stilled that was pow'r-ful in song— I steal all a-lone to Je-sus.

4. When my heart needs re-fresh-ing, my mind seeks for balm; When my striv-ings ail pale, and my wish is for calm, And the song of my heart should be a sweet psalm, I steal all a-lone to Je-sus.

CHORUS

All a-lone, all a-lone (all a-lone), All a-lone with Je-sus; The lights are made dim while com-mun-ing with Him, All a-lone (All a-lone), a-lone with Him......

I NEED JESUS

GEORGE O. WEBSTER

CHAS. H. GABRIEL

1. I need Je-sus, my need I now con-fess; No friend like Him in
2. I need Je-sus, I need a friend like Him, A friend to guide when
3. I need Je-sus, I need Him to the end; No one like Him—He

times of deep dis-tress; I need Je-sus, the need I glad-ly
paths of life are dim; I need Je-sus when foes my soul as
is the sin-ners' Friend; I need Je-sus, no oth-er friend will

own; Tho' some may bear their load a-lone, Yet I need Je-sus.
sail; A lone I know I can but fail,—So I need Je-sus,
do; So con-stant, kind, so strong, and true,—Yes, I need Je-sus,

CHORUS

I need Je-sus, I need Je-sus, I need Je-sus ev'ry
I need Je-sus with me I need Je-sus al-ways,

day; . . . . Need Him in the sunshine hour, need Him when the
ev-'ry day;

storm-clouds low'r; Ev - 'ry day a - long my way, Yes, I need Je - sus.

33 LET THE LOWER LIGHTS BE BURNING

P. P. B.

P. P. BLISS

1. Bright-ly beams our Fa-ther's mer-cy From His lighthouse ev - er - more;
2. Dark the night of sin has set-tled, Loud the an - gry bil-lows roar;
3. Trim your fee - ble lamp, my brother! Some poor sea - man, tempest-tossed,

But to us He gives the keep-ing Of the lights a - long the shore.
Ea - ger eyes are watching, long-ing, For the lights a - long the shore.
Try - ing now to make the har-bor, In the dark-ness may be lost.

CHORUS

Let the low - er lights be burning! Send a gleam a-cross the wave!

Some poor fainting, struggling sea-man You may res - cue, you may save.

HELP SOMEBODY TO-DAY

MRS. FRANK M. BRECK

CHAS. H. GABRIEL

1. Look all around you, find some one in need, Help somebod-y to - day!
2. Man - y are wait-ing a kind, lov-ing word, Help somebod-y to - day!
3. Man - y have bur-dens too heav - y to bear, Help somebod-y to - day!
4. Some are dis-cour-aged and wea - ry in heart, Help somebod-y to - day!

Tho' it be lit - tle— a neigh-bor - ly deed— Help somebod-y to - day!
Thou hast a mes-sage, O let it be heard, Help somebod-y to - day!
Grief is the por-tion of some ev - 'ry where, Help somebod-y to ·· day!
Some one the jour-ney to heav-en should start, Help somebod-y to - day!

CHORUS

Help somebod - y to - day,........ Some-bod - y a-long life's way;...... Let
to - day, homeward way;

sor-row be end-ed, The friendless befriended, Oh, help somebody to - day!

35 ON THE OTHER SIDE

T. O. Chisholm **Haldor Lillenas**

1. On the oth-er side is a land of won-der, Wa-tered by un-
2. Rest and home are there for the worn and wea-ry Bear-ing earth-ly
3. Ea-ger-ly we look, but our eyes are hold-en, Lis-ten-ing, we
4. Lin-ger we a-while in the place of du-ty, Just a lit-tle
5. Life and love are there far be-yond our know-ing, Pleas-ures un-al-

fail-ing streams; There the part-ed meet, torn by death a-sun-der,—
bur-dens long; Burst of ra-diant morn aft-er night time drear-y,
fail to hear, Things our God pre-pares in that cit-y gold-en,
more of prayer, Then to fly a-way to that land of beau-ty,
loyed with pain, Har-vest-ing with joy aft-er tear-ful sow-ing,

CHORUS

Oh, how near it some-times seems.
Wel-come to the white-robed throng.
On-ly faith can bring them near. On the oth-er side of the roll-ing tide
And the joys that wait us there.
Loss-es re-com-pensed with gain.

We shall meet and sing with the glo-ri-fied; We shall see the Lord and be

sat-is-fied! Ev-'ry-thing will be all right on the oth-er side.

WHEN LOVE SHINES IN

Mrs. Frank A. Breck   Wm. J. Kirkpatrick

1. Je - sus comes with pow'r to gladden, When love shines in,   Ev - 'ry life that
2. How the world will glow with beauty, When love shines in,   And the heart re-
3. Dark-est sor-row will grow brighter, When love shines in,   And the heav-iest
4. We may have un-fad-ing splen-dor, When love shines in,   And a friend-ship

woe can sad-den, When love shines in.   Love will teach us how to pray,
joice in du - ty, When love shines in.   Tri - als may be sanc - ti - fied,
bur - den light-er, When love shines in.   'Tis the glo - ry that will throw
true and ten - der, When love shines in.   When earth-vic-t'ries shall be won,

Love will drive the gloom away, Turn our darkness in - to day, When love shines in.
And the soul in peace a-bide, Life will all be glo - ri-fied, When love shines in.
Light to show us where to go; O the heart shall blessing know When love shines in.
And our life in heav'n begun, There will be no need of sun, For love shines in.

CHORUS

When love shines in, .. When love shines in, .. How the heart is

When love shines in, ...

When love shines in, When love shines in,   When love shines in, ..

tuned to singing, When love shines in; .. When love shines in, ... When

When love shines in; ..   When love shines in, ...

When love shines in, When love shines in,

WHEN LOVE SHINES IN

love shines in, Joy and peace to others bringing, When love shines in.
When love shines in, When love shines in.

37   SEAL US, O HOLY SPIRIT

COPYRIGHT, 1928, BY TULLAR-MEREDITH CO. RENEWAL

(*Inscribed to my friend, Rev. J. F. Carson, D. D.*)

THE LORENZ PUB. CO., OWNER

I. H. M.   *Prayerfully*   I. H. Meredith

1. Seal us, O Ho-ly Spir-it, Grant us Thine im-press, we pray;
2. Seal us, O Ho-ly Spir-it, Help us Thy like-ness to show;
3. Seal us, O Ho-ly Spir-it, Make us Thine own from this hour;

We would be more like the Sav-ior, Stamped with His im-age to-day.
Then from our lives un-to oth-ers Streams of rich bless-ings shall flow.
May we be use-ful, dear Mas-ter, Seal us with wit-ness-ing pow'r.

CHORUS

Seal us, seal us, Seal us just now, we pray; Seal us, O

rit.

Ho-ly Spir-it, Seal us for serv-ice to-day.

E. R. Wilberforce   H. R. Palmer

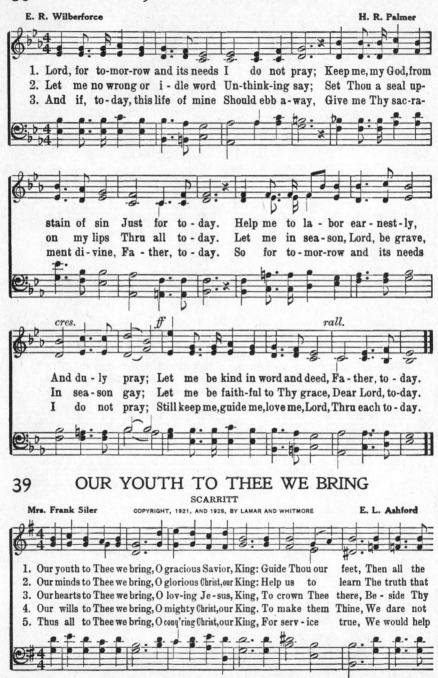

1. Lord, for to-mor-row and its needs I   do not pray; Keep me, my God, from
2. Let me no wrong or i - dle word Un-think-ing say; Set Thou a seal up-
3. And if, to-day, this life of mine Should ebb a-way, Give me Thy sac-ra-

stain of sin Just for to - day. Help me to la - bor ear - nest-ly,
on my lips Thru all to - day. Let me in sea - son, Lord, be grave,
ment di - vine, Fa - ther, to - day. So for to - mor-row and its needs

cres.   ff   rall.

And du - ly   pray; Let me be kind in word and deed, Fa - ther, to - day.
In sea - son gay; Let me be faith-ful to Thy grace, Dear Lord, to-day.
I   do not pray; Still keep me, guide me, love me, Lord, Thru each to - day.

39   OUR YOUTH TO THEE WE BRING
                          SCARRITT
Mrs. Frank Siler   COPYRIGHT, 1921, AND 1928, BY LAMAR AND WHITMORE   E. L. Ashford

1. Our youth to Thee we bring, O gracious Savior, King: Guide Thou our   feet, Then all the
2. Our minds to Thee we bring, O glorious Christ, our King: Help us   to   learn The truth that
3. Our hearts to Thee we bring, O lov-ing Je-sus, King, To crown Thee there, Be - side Thy
4. Our wills to Thee we bring, O mighty Christ, our King. To make them Thine, We dare not
5. Thus all to Thee we bring, O conq'ring Christ, our King, For serv - ice true, We would help

OUR YOUTH TO THEE WE BRING

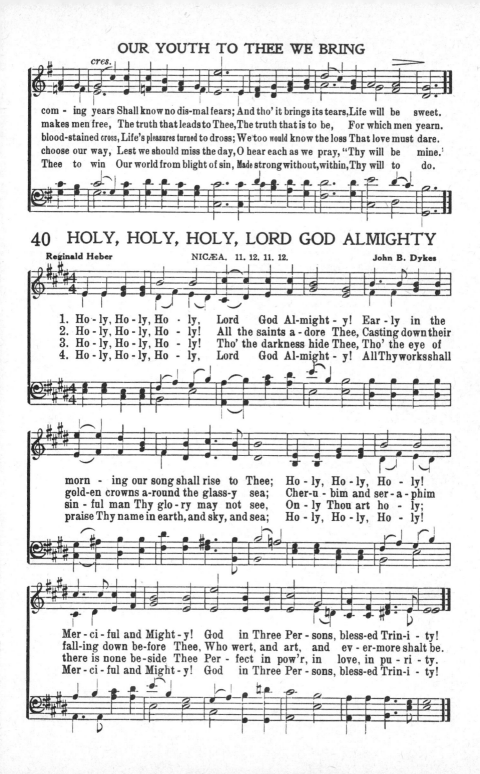

cres.

com - ing years Shall know no dis-mal fears; And tho' it brings its tears, Life will be sweet.
makes men free, The truth that leads to Thee, The truth that is to be, For which men yearn.
blood-stained cross, Life's pleasures turned to dross; We too would know the loss That love must dare.
choose our way, Lest we should miss the day, O hear each as we pray, "Thy will be mine."
Thee to win Our world from blight of sin, Made strong without, within, Thy will to do.

40 HOLY, HOLY, HOLY, LORD GOD ALMIGHTY

Reginald Heber   NICÆA. 11. 12. 11. 12.   John B. Dykes

1. Ho - ly, Ho - ly, Ho - ly, Lord God Al-might - y! Ear - ly in the
2. Ho - ly, Ho - ly, Ho - ly! All the saints a - dore Thee, Casting down their
3. Ho - ly, Ho - ly, Ho - ly! Tho' the darkness hide Thee, Tho' the eye of
4. Ho - ly, Ho - ly, Ho - ly, Lord God Al-might - y! All Thy works shall

morn - ing our song shall rise to Thee; Ho - ly, Ho - ly, Ho - ly!
gold-en crowns a-round the glass-y sea; Cher-u - bim and ser - a - phim
sin - ful man Thy glo-ry may not see, On - ly Thou art ho - ly;
praise Thy name in earth, and sky, and sea; Ho - ly, Ho - ly, Ho - ly!

Mer - ci - ful and Might - y! God in Three Per - sons, bless-ed Trin-i - ty!
fall-ing down be-fore Thee, Who wert, and art, and ev - er-more shalt be.
there is none be-side Thee Per - fect in pow'r, in love, in pu - ri - ty.
Mer - ci - ful and Might - y! God in Three Per - sons, bless-ed Trin-i - ty!

41 HALLELUJAH! WHAT A SAVIOR

P. P. B.

P. P. Bliss

1. "Man of sor-row," what a name For the Son of God who came
2. Bear - ing shame and scoff - ing rude, In my place condemned He stood,
3. Guilt - y, vile and help - less we; Spot - less Lamb of God was He;
4. Lift - ed up was He to die, "It is finished," was His cry;
5. When He comes, our glo - rious King, All His ransomed home to bring,

Ru - ined sin - ners to re-claim! Hal - le - lu - jah! what a Sav - ior!
Sealed my par - don with His blood; Hal - le - lu - jah! what a Sav - ior!
"Full a - tone-ment!" can it be? Hal - le - lu - jah! what a Sav - ior!
Now in heav'n ex - alt - ed high, Hal - le - lu - jah! what a Sav - ior!
Then a - new this song we'll sing, Hal - le - lu - jah! what a Sav - ior!

42 O DAY OF REST AND GLADNESS

Christopher Wordsworth   MENDEBRAS 7. 6. 7. 6. D.   Arr. by Lowell Mason

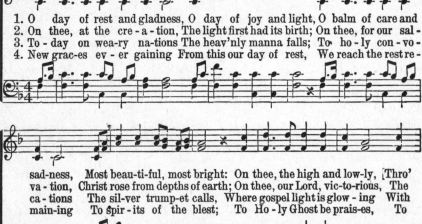

1. O day of rest and gladness, O day of joy and light, O balm of care and
2. On thee, at the cre - a - tion, The light first had its birth; On thee, for our sal -
3. To - day on wea - ry na-tions The heav'nly manna falls; To ho - ly con - vo -
4. New grac-es ev - er gaining From this our day of rest, We reach the rest re -

sad-ness, Most beau-ti-ful, most bright: On thee, the high and low-ly, [Thro'
va - tion, Christ rose from depths of earth; On thee, our Lord, vic-to-rious, The
ca - tions The sil-ver trump-et calls, Where gospel light is glow - ing With
main-ing To spir - its of the blest; To Ho - ly Ghost be prais-es, To

O DAY OF REST AND GLADNESS

a - ges joined in tune, Sing "Ho-ly, ho-ly, ho-ly," To the great God Tri-une.
Spirit sent from heav'n; And thus on Thee, most glorious, A tri - ple light was giv'n.
pure and radiant beams, And liv-ing wa-ter flow-ing With soul-re-fresh-ing streams.
Fa-ther, and to Son; The church her voice upraises To Thee, blest Three in One.

43   WHEN MORNING GILDS THE SKIES

Translated from the German by Edward Caswall

Joseph Barnby

1. When morn-ing gilds the skies, My heart a - wak-ing cries,
2. When-e'er the sweet church bell Peals o - ver hill and dell
3. The night be-comes as day, When from the heart we say,
4. In heav'n's e - ter - nal bliss The love- liest strain is this,
5. Be this, while life is mine, My can - ti - cle di - vine,

May Je - sus Christ be praised! A - like at work and pray'r,
May Je - sus Christ be praised! Oh! hark to what it sings,
May Je - sus Christ be praised! The pow'rs of dark-ness fear,
May Je - sus Christ be praised! Let earth, and sea, and sky,
May Je - sus Christ be praised! Be this th'e-ter-nal song

To Je - sus I re - pair; May Je - sus Christ be praised!
As joy - ous-ly it rings, May Je - sus Christ be praised!
When this sweet chant they hear, May Je - sus Christ be praised!
From depth to height re - ply, May Je - sus Christ be praised!
Through all the a - ges long, May Je - sus Christ be praised! A-men.

DAY IS DYING IN THE WEST

MARY A. LATHBURY

WILLIAM F. SHERWIN

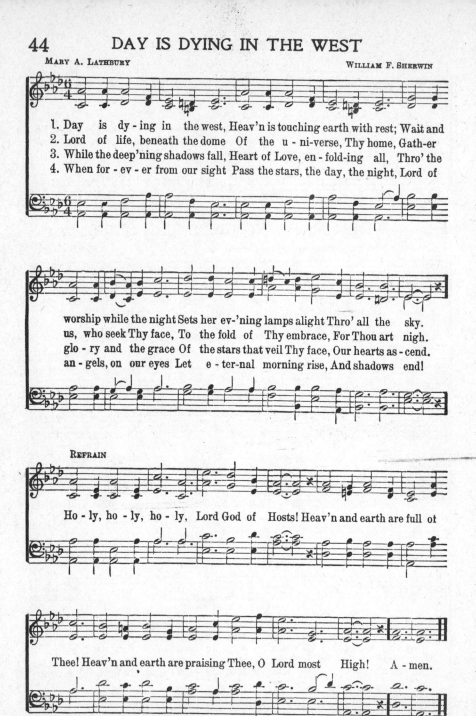

1. Day is dy-ing in the west, Heav'n is touching earth with rest; Wait and
2. Lord of life, beneath the dome Of the u-ni-verse, Thy home, Gath-er
3. While the deep'ning shadows fall, Heart of Love, en-fold-ing all, Thro' the
4. When for-ev-er from our sight Pass the stars, the day, the night, Lord of

worship while the night Sets her ev-'ning lamps alight Thro' all the sky.
us, who seek Thy face, To the fold of Thy embrace, For Thou art nigh.
glo-ry and the grace Of the stars that veil Thy face, Our hearts as-cend.
an-gels, on our eyes Let e-ter-nal morning rise, And shadows end!

REFRAIN

Ho-ly, ho-ly, ho-ly, Lord God of Hosts! Heav'n and earth are full of

Thee! Heav'n and earth are praising Thee, O Lord most High! A-men.

45 NOW THE DAY IS OVER

Sabine Baring-Gould

Joseph Barnby

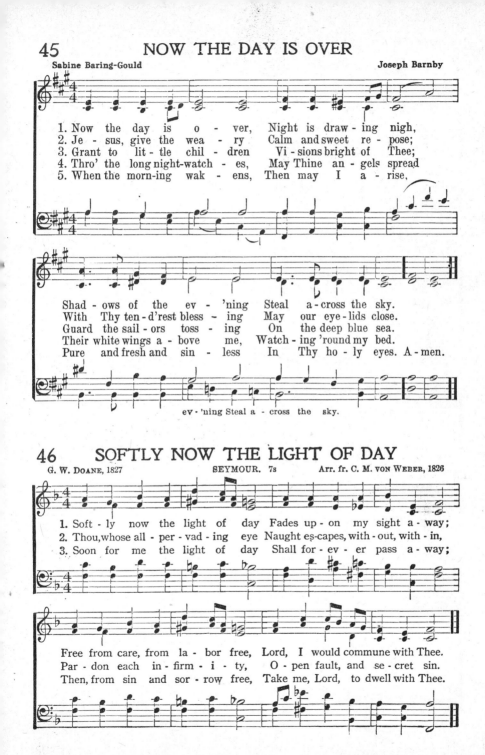

1. Now the day is o - ver, Night is draw - ing nigh,
2. Je - sus, give the wea - ry Calm and sweet re - pose;
3. Grant to lit - tle chil - dren Vi - sions bright of Thee;
4. Thro' the long night-watch - es, May Thine an - gels spread
5. When the morn-ing wak - ens, Then may I a - rise,

Shad - ows of the ev - 'ning Steal a - cross the sky.
With Thy ten - d'rest bless - ing May our eye - lids close.
Guard the sail - ors toss - ing On the deep blue sea.
Their white wings a - bove me, Watch - ing 'round my bed.
Pure and fresh and sin - less In Thy ho - ly eyes. A - men.

ev - 'ning Steal a - cross the sky.

46 SOFTLY NOW THE LIGHT OF DAY

G. W. DOANE, 1827   SEYMOUR. 7s   Arr. fr. C. M. VON WEBER, 1826

1. Soft - ly now the light of day Fades up - on my sight a - way;
2. Thou, whose all - per - vad - ing eye Naught es - capes, with - out, with - in,
3. Soon for me the light of day Shall for - ev - er pass a - way;

Free from care, from la - bor free, Lord, I would commune with Thee.
Par - don each in - firm - i - ty, O - pen fault, and se - cret sin.
Then, from sin and sor - row free, Take me, Lord, to dwell with Thee.

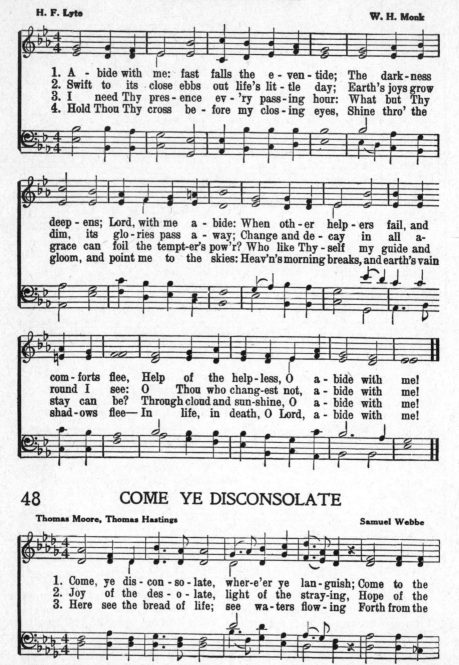

47   ABIDE WITH ME

H. F. Lyte

W. H. Monk

1. A - bide with me: fast falls the e - ven - tide; The dark - ness
2. Swift to its close ebbs out life's lit - tle day; Earth's joys grow
3. I need Thy pres - ence ev - 'ry pass - ing hour: What but Thy
4. Hold Thou Thy cross be - fore my clos - ing eyes, Shine thro' the

deep - ens; Lord, with me a - bide: When oth - er help - ers fail, and
dim, its glo - ries pass a - way; Change and de - cay in all a -
grace can foil the tempt - er's pow'r? Who like Thy - self my guide and
gloom, and point me to the skies: Heav'n's morning breaks, and earth's vain

com - forts flee, Help of the help - less, O a - bide with me!
round I see: O Thou who chang - est not, a - bide with me!
stay can be? Through cloud and sun - shine, O a - bide with me!
shad - ows flee— In life, in death, O Lord, a - bide with me!

48   COME YE DISCONSOLATE

Thomas Moore, Thomas Hastings

Samuel Webbe

1. Come, ye dis - con - so - late, wher-e'er ye lan - guish; Come to the
2. Joy of the des - o - late, light of the stray - ing, Hope of the
3. Here see the bread of life; see wa - ters flow - ing Forth from the

COME, YE DISCONSOLATE

mer - cy - seat, fer - vent - ly kneel; Here bring your wound-ed hearts,
pen - i - tent, fade - less and pure, Here speaks the Com - fort - er,
throne of God, pure from a - bove; Come to the feast of love;

here tell your an - guish; Earth has no sor-row that Heav'n can-not heal.
ten - der-ly say - ing, "Earth has no sor-row that Heav'n can-not cure."
come, ev - er know-ing Earth has no sor-row but Heav'n can re - move.

49 SUN OF MY SOUL

JOHN KEBLE

PETER RITTER

1. Sun of my soul! Thou Sav-ior dear, It is not night if Thou be near;
2. When the soft dews of kind-ly sleep My wea-ry eye-lids gen-tly steep,
3. A - bide with me from morn till eve, For with-out Thee I can-not live;
4. Be near to bless me when I wake, Ere thro' the world my way I take;

Oh, may no earth-born cloud a - rise To hide Thee from Thy servant's eyes!
Be my last tho't—how sweet to rest For-ev - er on my Savior's breast!
A - bide with me when night is nigh, For without Thee I dare not die.
A - bide with me till in Thy love I lose my - self in heav'n a-bove.

50 THE CHURCH'S ONE FOUNDATION

SAMUEL J. STONE

SAMUEL S. WESLEY

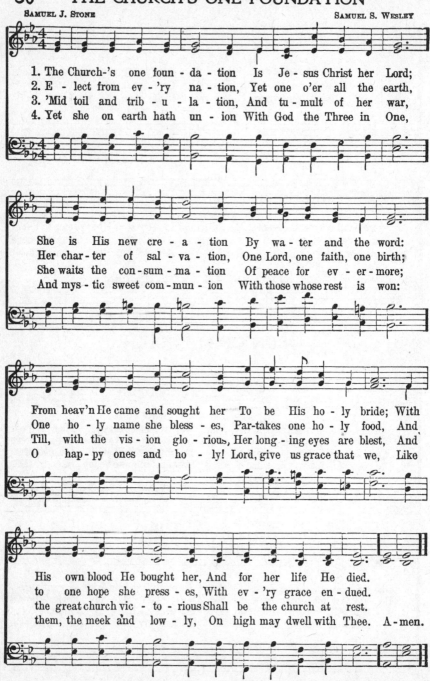

1. The Church-'s one foun - da - tion   Is Je - sus Christ her Lord;
2. E - lect from ev - 'ry na - tion, Yet one o'er all the earth,
3. 'Mid toil and trib - u - la - tion, And tu - mult of her war,
4. Yet she on earth hath un - ion With God the Three in One,

She is His new cre - a - tion   By wa - ter and the word:
Her char - ter of sal - va - tion,   One Lord, one faith, one birth;
She waits the con - sum - ma - tion   Of peace for   ev - er - more;
And mys - tic sweet com - mun - ion With those whose rest is won:

From heav'n He came and sought her   To be His ho - ly bride; With
One   ho - ly name she bless - es, Par-takes one ho - ly food, And
Till, with the vis - ion glo - rious, Her long - ing eyes are blest, And
O   hap - py ones and ho - ly! Lord, give us grace that we, Like

His own blood He bought her, And for her life He died.
to   one hope she press - es, With ev - 'ry grace en - dued.
the great church vic - to - rious Shall be the church at rest.
them, the meek and low - ly, On high may dwell with Thee. A - men.

51 OH! WHERE ARE KINGS AND EMPIRES NOW

A. Cleveland Coxe   ST. ANNE C. M.   William Croft

1. Oh! where are kings and em - pires now, Of old that went and came?
2. We mark her good - ly bat - tle-ments, And her foun - da - tions strong;
3. For not like king-doms of the world Thy ho - ly Church, O God!
4. Un - shak - en as e - ter - nal hills, Im-mov - a - ble she stands,

But, Lord, Thy Church is pray-ing yet, A thou-sand years the same.
We hear with - in the sol-emn voice Of her un - end-ing song.
Tho' earthquake shocks are threat'ning her, And tempests are a-broad;
A moun-tain that shall fill the earth, A house not made with hands. A - men.

52 I LOVE THY KINGDOM, LORD

Timothy Dwight   ST. THOMAS S. M.   Aaron Williams, Collection

1. I love Thy king - dom, Lord, The house of Thine a - bode,
2. I love Thy Church, O God! Her walls be - fore Thee stand,
3. For her my tears shall fall; For her my pray'rs as - cend;
4. Be - yond my high - est joy I prize her heav'nly ways,
5. Sure as Thy truth shall last, To Zi - on shall be giv'n

The Church our blest Redeemer saved With His own pre-cious blood.
Dear as the ap - ple of Thine eye, And grav-en on Thy hand.
To her my cares and toils be giv'n; Till toils and cares shall end.
Her sweet com-mun-ion, solemn vows, Her hymns of love and praise.
The brightest glories earth can yield, And brighter bliss of heav'n. A - men.

53 GO FORWARD

H. L.

Haldor Lillenas

1. For the cause of right we've en-list-ed to fight In the ar-mies of our
2. In the gra-cious past in this ar-my so vast God has led us 'gainst the
3. Great our might-y foe, in the world here be-low, But our Cap-tain nev-er

Lord and King; Marching on we go, brave-ly fac'-ing the foe, Hear the
hosts of sin; Now we for-ward face, and by His wondrous grace There a-
knew de-feat; He will lead us on till the bright, golden dawn, When the

bat-tle-cry of vic-t'ry loud-ly ring!
wait us man-y vic-t'ries yet to win.
bat-tles of our life shall be com-plete;

CHORUS *Unison*

"Go for-ward, and on-ward!" Nev-er
know-ing de-feat, nev-er sound-ing re-treat. Go for-ward and on-ward, In the

Four parts

name of God's dear Son! .. Go for-ward and on-ward, Un-til sin be back-ward

GO FORWARD

hurled,.. Until the banner of full salvation Shall float above the wide, wide world.
back-ward hurled,

54 I AM DETERMINED

Haldor Lillenas   Bertha Mae Lillenas

1. I am de-ter-mined to fol-low Je-sus, Walk-ing the nar-row way,
2. I am de-ter-mined to do His bid-ding, What-ev-er that may be;
3. I am de-ter-mined to seek His coun-sel, When dim my path may seem;
4. I am de-ter-mined to tell the sto-ry, Sto-ry of love di-vine;

Find-ing my great-est joy in serv-ing Faith-ful-ly ev-'ry day.
Know-ing what-ev-er He de-sir-eth Al-ways is best for me.
Soon will the drear-y shad-ows van-ish, And gold-en sun-light gleam.
So   that in hearts now dark and drear-y Light, gos-pel light may shine.

Chorus

I am determined to go where He leads me, To work where He needs me; Loyal for-

ev-er; Faith-ful-ly liv-ing, serving and giv-ing All of my life to Thee.

55 GLORIOUS THINGS OF THEE ARE SPOKEN

John Newton   AUSTRIA 8. 7. 8. 7. D.   Francis J. Haydn

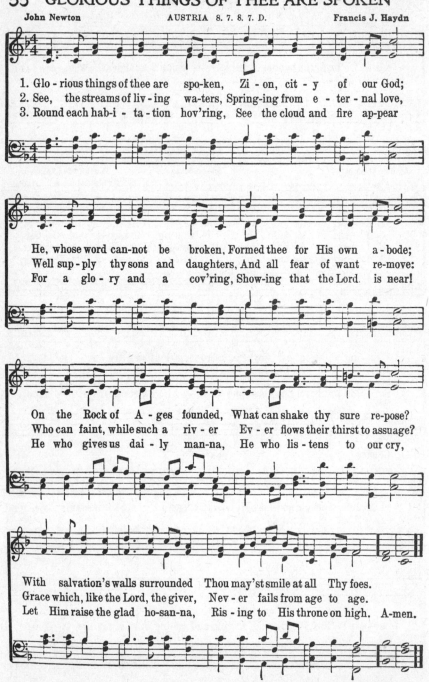

1. Glo - rious things of thee are spo-ken, Zi - on, cit - y of our God;
2. See, the streams of liv-ing wa-ters, Spring-ing from e - ter - nal love,
3. Round each hab-i - ta-tion hov'ring, See the cloud and fire ap-pear

He, whose word can-not be broken, Formed thee for His own a - bode!
Well sup - ply thy sons and daughters, And all fear of want re-move:
For a glo - ry and a cov'ring, Show-ing that the Lord is near!

On the Rock of A - ges founded, What can shake thy sure re-pose?
Who can faint, while such a riv - er Ev - er flows their thirst to assuage?
He who gives us dai - ly man-na, He who lis - tens to our cry,

With salvation's walls surrounded Thou may'st smile at all Thy foes.
Grace which, like the Lord, the giver, Nev - er fails from age to age.
Let Him raise the glad ho-san-na, Ris - ing to His throne on high. A-men.

56 GOD WILL TAKE CARE OF YOU

(Dedicated to my wife, Mrs. John A. Davis)

C. D. Martin   W. S. Martin

1. Be not dis - mayed whate'er be - tide, God will take care of you;
2. Thro' days of toil when heart doth fail, God will take care of you;
3. All you may need He will pro - vide, God will take care of you;
4. No mat - ter what may be the test, God will take care of you;

Be - neath His wings of love a - bide, God will take care of you.
When dangers fierce your path as - sail, God will take care of you.
Noth - ing you ask will be de - nied, God will take care of you.
Lean, wea - ry one, up - on His breast, God will take care of you.

CHORUS

God will take care of you, Thro' ev - 'ry day, O'er all the way;

He will take care of you, God will take care of you.......
take care of you.

57 THY WORD, O LORD, IS MY DELIGHT

COPYRIGHT, 1929, BY HOMER A. RODEHEAVER

Charlotte G. Homer

Chas. H. Gabriel

1. Thy Word, O Lord, is my de-light, 'Tis man-na to my hun-gry soul;
2. Its pag-es teem with sa-cred lore, From which all wis-dom is con-ferred;
3. It guards me from the tempter's snare, And coun-sels wis-er than a friend;
4. It is a treas-ure house of gold, From whose supplies I would not part;
5. O Book of Life, of Love and Truth, My hope of heav'n I find in thee;

It is a nev-er-fail-ing light That marks the reef and rock-y shoal.
It grows in splen-dor more and more, This Book of books, God's Ho-ly Word.
It com-forts grief and light-ens care, Its yield of rich-es has no end.
It gives re-turns a thou-sand fold, When plant-ed in the hu-man heart.
The on-ly guide of age and youth, The Word of God—His gift to me.

REFRAIN

"Ho-ly Bi-ble, Book di-vine, Pre-cious treas-ure, thou art mine."

58 LAMP OF OUR FEET

Bernard Barton

Temple Melodies

1. Lamp of our feet, where-by we trace Our path when wont to stray;
2. Bread of our souls, where-on we feed, True man-na from on high;
3. Word of the ev-er-last-ing God, Will of His glo-rious Son;
4. Lord, grant us all a-right to learn The wis-dom it im-parts.

LAMP OF OUR FEET

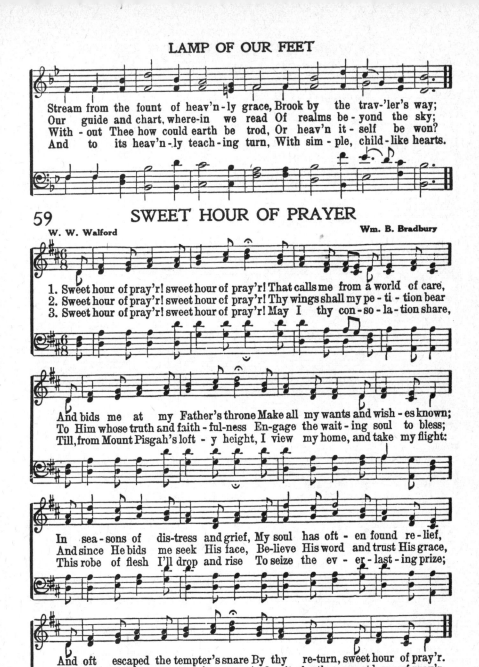

Stream from the fount of heav'n-ly grace, Brook by the trav-'ler's way;
Our guide and chart, where-in we read Of realms be-yond the sky;
With-out Thee how could earth be trod, Or heav'n it-self be won?
And to its heav'n-ly teach-ing turn, With sim-ple, child-like hearts.

59 SWEET HOUR OF PRAYER

W. W. Walford

Wm. B. Bradbury

1. Sweet hour of pray'r! sweet hour of pray'r! That calls me from a world of care,
2. Sweet hour of pray'r! sweet hour of pray'r! Thy wings shall my pe-ti-tion bear
3. Sweet hour of pray'r! sweet hour of pray'r! May I thy con-so-la-tion share,

And bids me at my Father's throne Make all my wants and wish-es known;
To Him whose truth and faith-ful-ness En-gage the wait-ing soul to bless;
Till, from Mount Pisgah's loft-y height, I view my home, and take my flight:

In sea-sons of dis-tress and grief, My soul has oft-en found re-lief,
And since He bids me seek His face, Be-lieve His word and trust His grace,
This robe of flesh I'll drop and rise To seize the ev-er-last-ing prize;

And oft escaped the tempter's snare By thy re-turn, sweet hour of pray'r.
I'll cast on Him my ev-'ry care, And wait for thee, sweet hour of pray'r.
And shout, while passing thro' the air, Farewell, farewell, sweet hour of pray'r.

O WORD OF GOD INCARNATE

Chenies.

William Walsham How, 1867.　　　　　Timothy R. Matthews, 1855.

1. O Word of God in - car - nate, O Wis - dom from on high,
2. The Church from her dear Mas - ter Re-ceived the gift di - vine,
3. It float - eth like a ban - ner Be - fore God's host un - furled;
4. O make Thy Church, dear Sav - ior, A lamp of pur - est gold,

O Truth un-changed, un-chang - ing, O Light of our dark sky,
And still that light she lift - eth O'er all the earth to shine.
It shin - eth like a bea - con A - bove the dark-ling world:
To bear be - fore the na - tions Thy true light as of old!

We praise thee for the ra - diance That from the hal-lowed page,
It is the gold - en cas - ket Where gems of truth are stored;
It is the chart and com - pass That o'er life's surg - ing sea,
O teach Thy wan-d'ring pil - grims By this their path to trace,

A lan-tern to our foot-steps, Shines on from age to age.
It is the heav'n-drawn pic-ture Of Christ the liv - ing Word.
'Mid mists and rocks and dark - ness, Still guides, O Christ, to Thee.
Till, clouds and dark-ness end - ed, They see Thee face to face! A-MEN.

61 THE STORY THAT NEVER GROWS OLD

A. H. A.

Rev. A. H. Ackley

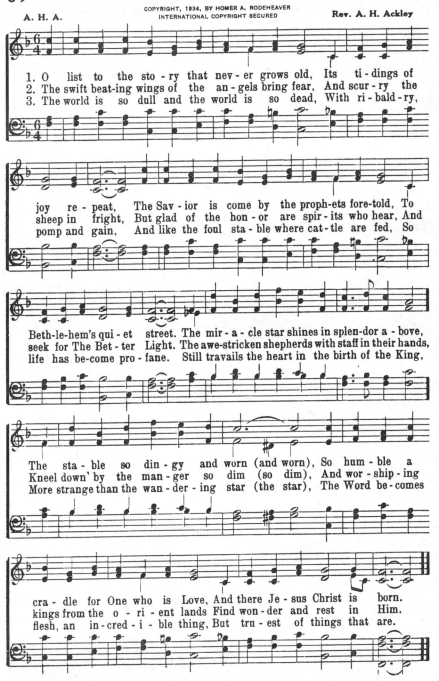

1. O list to the sto-ry that nev-er grows old, Its ti-dings of joy re-peat, The Sav-ior is come by the proph-ets fore-told, To Beth-le-hem's qui-et street. The mir-a-cle star shines in splen-dor a-bove, The sta-ble so din-gy and worn (and worn), So hum-ble a cra-dle for One who is Love, And there Je-sus Christ is born.

2. The swift beat-ing wings of the an-gels bring fear, And scur-ry the sheep in fright, But glad of the hon-or are spir-its who hear, And seek for The Bet-ter Light. The awe-stricken shepherds with staff in their hands, Kneel down by the man-ger so dim (so dim), And wor-ship-ing kings from the o-ri-ent lands Find won-der and rest in Him.

3. The world is so dull and the world is so dead, With ri-bald-ry, pomp and gain, And like the foul sta-ble where cat-tle are fed, So life has be-come pro-fane. Still travails the heart in the birth of the King, More strange than the wan-der-ing star (the star), The Word be-comes flesh, an in-cred-i-ble thing, But tru-est of things that are.

62 O HOLY DAY OF PENTECOST

To Dr. Jesse M. Bader, in appreciation of his life's work; and, who suggested the writing of the hymn.

F. C. H.

Frank C. Huston

With devotion

1. O ho-ly day of Pen-te-cost, On which the Spir-it came,
2. O glo-rious day of Pen-te-cost; O bless-ed na-tal morn,
3. O bless-ed Lord of Pen-te-cost, Our Sav-ior and our King,
4. Lead us, O Lord, by Thy rich grace, And keep us all from sin;

In prom-ised pow'r as anx-ious hearts Were met in Je-sus' name.
When, in the hearts of ho-ly men, The Church of Christ was born.
To Thee, for all Thy gifts of love, Our grate-ful hearts we bring.
We would re-mem-ber Cal-va-ry,—Reign Thou, our hearts with-in.

O won-drous gift the Fa-ther sent To those who tar-ried there,
O bless-ed day when heav'n and earth Were met with one ac-cord,
O fill us with Thy Spir-it, Lord, And keep us ev-er true,
Thy wondrous grace we would de-clare; Thy won-drous love make known,

O-be-dient to their Lord's command, In wait-ing and in prayer.
In might-y pow'r, to her-ald forth The king-dom of our Lord.
That we shall be Thy wit-ness-es In all we are and do.
Till, with the ran-somed hosts a-bove, We praise Thee on Thy throne.

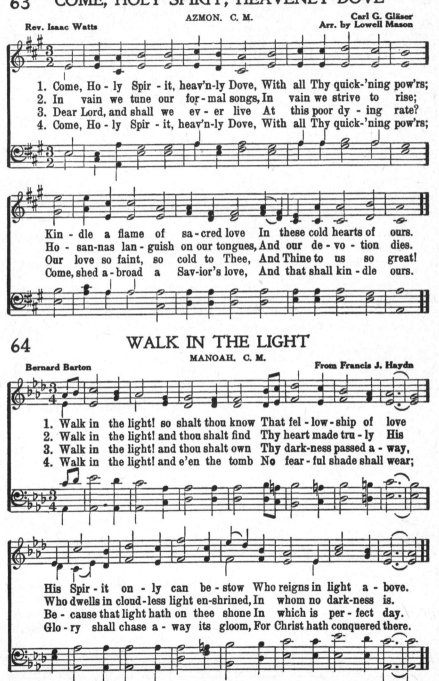

63 COME, HOLY SPIRIT, HEAVENLY DOVE

AZMON. C. M.

Rev. Isaac Watts

Carl G. Gläser
Arr. by Lowell Mason

1. Come, Ho - ly Spir - it, heav'n-ly Dove, With all Thy quick-'ning pow'rs;
2. In vain we tune our for - mal songs, In vain we strive to rise;
3. Dear Lord, and shall we ev - er live At this poor dy - ing rate?
4. Come, Ho - ly Spir - it, heav'n-ly Dove, With all Thy quick-'ning pow'rs;

Kin - dle a flame of sa - cred love In these cold hearts of ours.
Ho - san-nas lan - guish on our tongues, And our de - vo - tion dies.
Our love so faint, so cold to Thee, And Thine to us so great!
Come, shed a - broad a Sav-ior's love, And that shall kin - dle ours.

64 WALK IN THE LIGHT

MANOAH. C. M.

Bernard Barton

From Francis J. Haydn

1. Walk in the light! so shalt thou know That fel - low - ship of love
2. Walk in the light! and thou shalt find Thy heart made tru - ly His
3. Walk in the light! and thou shalt own Thy dark-ness passed a - way,
4. Walk in the light! and e'en the tomb No fear - ful shade shall wear;

His Spir - it on - ly can be - stow Who reigns in light a - bove.
Who dwells in cloud - less light en-shrined, In whom no dark-ness is.
Be - cause that light hath on thee shone In which is per - fect day.
Glo - ry shall chase a - way its gloom, For Christ hath conquered there.

SAVIOR, MORE THAN LIFE

FANNY J. CROSBY

W. H. DOANE

1. Sav - ior, more than life to me, I am clinging, clinging close to Thee;
2. Thro' this changing world be - low, Lead me gen-tly, gen-tly as I go;
3. Let me love Thee more and more, Till this fleeting, fleeting life is o'er,

FINE

Let Thy pre-cious blood ap-plied; Keep me ev - er, ev - er near Thy side.
Trusting Thee, I can-not stray, I can nev-er, nev-er lose my way.
Till my soul is lost in love, In a brighter, brighter world a - bove.

D. S.—May Thy ten - der love to me Bind me clos - er, clos - er, Lord, to Thee.

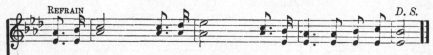

REFRAIN

D. S.

Ev'-ry day, ev - 'ry hour, Let me feel Thy cleansing pow'r;
Ev - 'ry day and hour, Ev - 'ry day and hour,

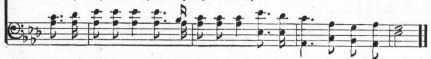

HOLY GHOST, WITH LIGHT DIVINE

A. REED

GOTTSCHALK

1. Ho - ly Ghost, with light di - vine, Shine up - on this heart of mine;
2. Ho - ly Ghost, with pow'r di - vine, Cleanse this guilt - y heart of mine;
3. Ho - ly Ghost, with joy di - vine, Cheer this saddened heart of mine;
4. Ho - ly Spir - it, all di - vine, Dwell with - in this heart of mine;

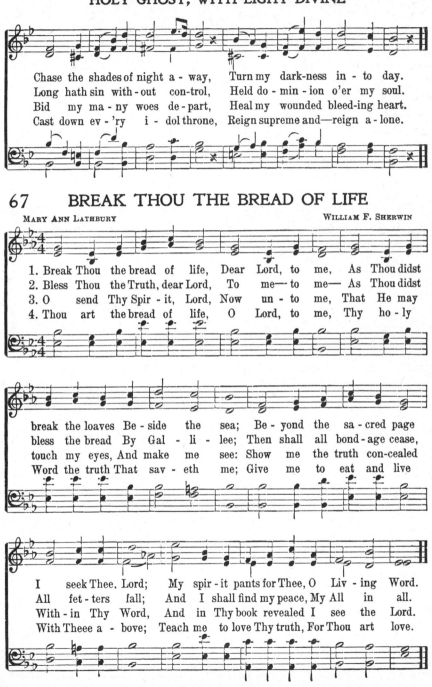

HOLY GHOST, WITH LIGHT DIVINE

Chase the shades of night a-way, Turn my dark-ness in-to day.
Long hath sin with-out con-trol, Held do-min-ion o'er my soul.
Bid my ma-ny woes de-part, Heal my wounded bleed-ing heart.
Cast down ev-'ry i-dol throne, Reign supreme and—reign a-lone.

67   BREAK THOU THE BREAD OF LIFE

MARY ANN LATHBURY   WILLIAM F. SHERWIN

1. Break Thou the bread of life, Dear Lord, to me, As Thou didst
2. Bless Thou the Truth, dear Lord, To me—to me— As Thou didst
3. O send Thy Spir-it, Lord, Now un-to me, That He may
4. Thou art the bread of life, O Lord, to me, Thy ho-ly

break the loaves Be-side the sea; Be-yond the sa-cred page
bless the bread By Gal-li-lee; Then shall all bond-age cease,
touch my eyes, And make me see: Show me the truth con-cealed
Word the truth That sav-eth me; Give me to eat and live

I seek Thee, Lord; My spir-it pants for Thee, O Liv-ing Word.
All fet-ters fall; And I shall find my peace, My All in all.
With-in Thy Word, And in Thy book revealed I see the Lord.
With Theee a-bove; Teach me to love Thy truth, For Thou art love.

PENTECOSTAL POWER

CHARLOTTE G. HOMER

CHAS. H. GABRIEL

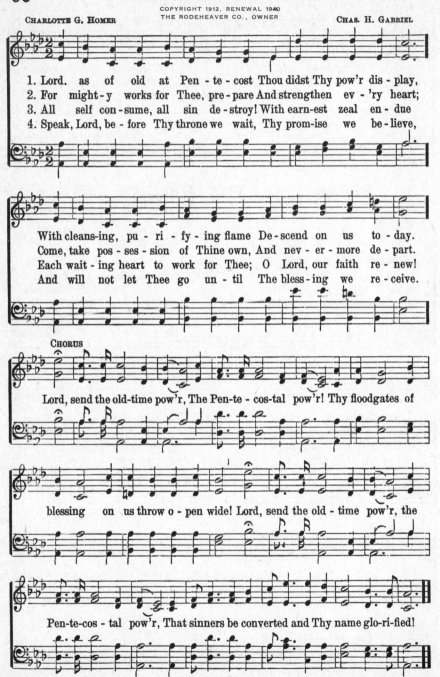

1. Lord, as of old at Pen - te - cost Thou didst Thy pow'r dis - play,
2. For might - y works for Thee, pre - pare And strengthen ev - 'ry heart;
3. All self con - sume, all sin de - stroy! With earn - est zeal en - due
4. Speak, Lord, be - fore Thy throne we wait, Thy prom - ise we be - lieve,

With cleans - ing, pu - ri - fy - ing flame De - scend on us to - day.
Come, take pos - ses - sion of Thine own, And nev - er - more de - part.
Each wait - ing heart to work for Thee; O Lord, our faith re - new!
And will not let Thee go un - til The bless - ing we re - ceive.

CHORUS

Lord, send the old-time pow'r, The Pen - te - cos - tal pow'r! Thy floodgates of

blessing on us throw o - pen wide! Lord, send the old - time pow'r, the

Pen - te - cos - tal pow'r, That sinners be converted and Thy name glo - ri - fied!

HOLY SPIRIT, FAITHFUL GUIDE

M. M. W.

M. M. Wells

FINE.

1. Ho - ly Spir - it, faith-ful Guide, Ev - er near the Chris-tian's side,
   Gen - tly lead us by the hand, Pil - grims in a des - ert land.
2. Ev - er pres - ent, tru - est Friend, Ev - er near Thine aid to lend,
   Leave us not to doubt and fear, Grop-ing on in dark-ness drear;
3. When our days of toil shall cease, Wait-ing still for sweet re - lease,
   Noth - ing left but heav'n and prayer, Won-d'ring if our names are there;

D.C.—Whisp'ring soft - ly, "Wand'rer, come! Fol - low Me, I'll guide thee home."
D.C.—Whis - per soft - ly, "Wand'rer, come! Fol - low Me, I'll guide thee home."
D.C.—Whis - per soft - ly, "Wand'rer, come! Fol - low Me, I'll guide thee home."

D. C.

Wea - ry souls for - e'er re - joice, While they hear the sweet-est voice,
When the storms are rag - ing sore, Hearts grow faint and hopes give o'er,
Wad - ing deep the dis - mal flood, Plead-ing naught but Je - sus' blood,

HOLY SPIRIT, FROM ON HIGH

W. H. Bathurst

C. M. von Weber

1. Ho - ly Spir - it, from on high, Bend o'er us a pity-ing eye;
2. Light up ev - 'ry dark re - cess Of our heart's un-god - li - ness;
3. Teach us, with re - pent - ant grief, Hum - bly to im - plore re - lief;
4. May we dai - ly grow in grace, And pur - sue the heav'n-ly race,

Now re - fresh the droop-ing heart; Bid the pow'r of sin de - part.
Show us ev - 'ry de - vious way Where our steps have gone a - stray.
Then the Sav - ior's blood re - veal, And our bro - ken spir - its heal.
Trained in wis - dom, led by love, Till we reach our rest a - bove.

71 OPEN MY EYES THAT I MAY SEE

Copyright, 1923. Renewal by H. F. Sayles, F. E. Hathaway, owner

C. H. S.

Clara H. Scott

1. O-pen my eyes, that I may see, Glimpses of truth Thou hast for me;
2. O-pen my ears, that I may hear, Voi-ces of truth Thou send-est clear;
3. O-pen my mouth and let me bear Glad-ly the warm truth ev - 'ry-where;

Place in my hands the won-der-ful key That shall unclasp, and set me free.
And while the wave-notes fall on my ear, Ev-'ry-thing false will dis - ap-pear.
O - pen my heart and let me prepare Love with Thy chil-dren thus to share.

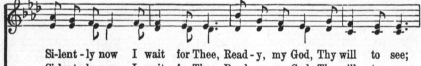

Si-lent-ly now I wait for Thee, Read-y, my God, Thy will to see;
Si-lent-ly now I wait for Thee, Read-y, my God, Thy will to see;
Si-lent-ly now I wait for Thee, Read-y, my God, Thy will to see;

O-pen my eyes, il - lu - mine me, Spir - it di - vine!
O-pen my ears, il - lu - mine me, Spir - it di - vine!
O-pen my heart, il - lu - mine me, Spir - it di - vine! A - men.

72 IN THE HOUR OF TRIAL

James Montgomery   Spencer Lane

1. In the hour of tri - al, Je - sus, plead for me, Lest by base de-
2. With for - bid - den pleas-ures Would this vain world charm, Or its sor - did
3. Should Thy mer-cy send me Sor - row, toil and woe, Or should pain at-

ni - al   I de-part from Thee; When Thou seest me wa - ver, With a
treas-ures Spread to work me harm, Bring to my re-membrance Sad Geth-
tend me On my path be - low, Grant that I may nev - er Fail Thy

look re - call, Nor for fear or fa - vor Suf - fer me to fall.
sem - a - ne, Or, in dark - er sem-blance, Cross-crowned Cal - va-ry.
hand to see; Grant that I may ev - er Cast my care on Thee.

73 OLD-TIME POWER

P. R.
Paul Rader

CHORUS

Spir - it, now melt and move All of our hearts with love,

Breathe on us from a - bove With old - time pow'r.

74 O MASTER, LET ME WALK WITH THEE

Washington Gladden   CANONBURY L. M.   Robert Schumann

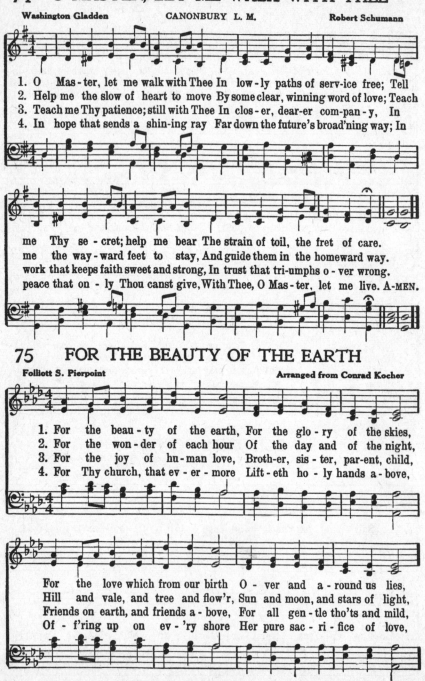

1. O Mas-ter, let me walk with Thee In low-ly paths of serv-ice free; Tell
2. Help me the slow of heart to move By some clear, winning word of love; Teach
3. Teach me Thy patience; still with Thee In clos-er, dear-er com-pan-y, In
4. In hope that sends a shin-ing ray Far down the future's broad'ning way; In

me Thy se - cret; help me bear The strain of toil, the fret of care.
me the way-ward feet to stay, And guide them in the homeward way.
work that keeps faith sweet and strong, In trust that tri-umphs o - ver wrong.
peace that on - ly Thou canst give, With Thee, O Mas-ter, let me live. A-MEN.

75 FOR THE BEAUTY OF THE EARTH

Folliott S. Pierpoint   Arranged from Conrad Kocher

1. For the beau - ty of the earth, For the glo - ry of the skies,
2. For the won - der of each hour Of the day and of the night,
3. For the joy of hu - man love, Broth - er, sis - ter, par - ent, child,
4. For Thy church, that ev - er - more Lift - eth ho - ly hands a - bove,

For the love which from our birth O - ver and a - round us lies,
Hill and vale, and tree and flow'r, Sun and moon, and stars of light,
Friends on earth, and friends a - bove, For all gen - tle tho'ts and mild,
Of - f'ring up on ev - 'ry shore Her pure sac - ri - fice of love,

FOR THE BEAUTY OF THE EARTH

REFRAIN

Lord of all, to Thee we raise This our hymn of grate-ful praise.

76   HOW FIRM A FOUNDATION

George Keith   Unknown

1. How firm a foun-da-tion, ye saints of the Lord, Is laid for your
2. "Fear not, I am with thee, O be not dis-mayed, For I am thy
3. "When thro' the deep wa-ters I call thee to go, The riv-ers of
4. "When thro' fier-y tri-als thy path-way shall lie, My grace, all-suf-

faith in His ex-cel-lent Word! What more can He say than to
God, I will still give thee aid; I'll strength-en thee, help thee, and
sor-row shall not o-ver-flow; For I will be with thee thy
fi-cient, shall be thy sup-ply, The flames shall not hurt thee: I

you He hath said, To you, who for ref-uge to Je-sus have
cause thee to stand, Up-held by My gra-cious, om-nip-o-tent
tri-als to bless, And sanc-ti-fy to thee thy deep-est dis-
on-ly de-sign Thy dross to con-sume, and thy gold to re-

fled? To you, who for ref-uge to Je-sus have fled?
hand, Up-held by My gra-cious, om-nip-o-tent hand.
tress, And sanc-ti-fy to thee thy deep-est dis-tress.
fine, Thy dross to con-sume, and thy gold to re-fine." A-men.

TRUSTING JESUS

E. Page

Ira D. Sankey

1. Sim - ply trust - ing ev - 'ry day, Trust - ing thru a storm - y way;
2. Bright-ly doth His Spir - it shine In - to this poor heart of mine;
3. Sing - ing if my way is clear; Pray - ing if the path be drear;
4. Trust-ing Him while life shall last, Trust-ing Him till earth be past;

E - ven when my faith is small, Trust-ing Je - sus, that is all.
While He leads I can - not fall; Trust-ing Je - sus, that is all.
If in dan - ger, for Him call; Trust-ing Je - sus, that is all.
Till with-in the jas - per wall: Trust-ing Je - sus, that is all.

CHORUS

Trust-ing as the mo-ments fly, Trust-ing as the days go by;

Trust-ing Him what-e'er be-fall, Trust-ing Je - sus, that is all.

78 HE'S THE ONE I LOVE

N. B. V.

COPYRIGHT, 1933, BY L. P. LEHMAN

N. B. Vandall

He's the One I love, . . . He's the One I love, ...

HE'S THE ONE I LOVE

Fair-er is He than the lil-y to me, He's the One I love.

79   BEAUTIFUL VALLEY OF EDEN

Walter O. Cushing

William F. Sherwin

1. Beau - ti - ful val - ley of E - den! Sweet is thy noon-tide calm;
2. O - ver the heart of the mourn-er Shin - eth thy gold - en day,
3. There is the home of my Sav - ior; There, with the blood-washed throng,

O - ver the heart of the wea - ry Breath-ing thy waves of balm.
Waft-ing the songs of the an - gels Down from the far - a - way.
O - ver the high-lands of glo - ry Roll - eth the great new song.

REFRAIN

Beau-ti-ful val - ley of E - den, Home of the pure and blest, How
the pure and blest,

rit.

oft - en a - mid the wild bil - lows I dream of thy rest, sweet rest!

PRAISE HIM! PRAISE HIM!

FANNY J. CROSBY

CHESTER G. ALLEN

1. Praise Him! praise Him! Je-sus, our bless-ed Re-deem-er! Sing, O Earth, His
2. Praise Him! praise Him! Je-sus, our bless-ed Re-deem-er! For our sins He
3. Praise Him! praise Him! Je-sus, our bless-ed Re-deem-er! Heav'nly por - tals

won-der-ful love pro-claim! Hail Him! hail Him! highest archangels in glo-ry;
suffered, and bled, and died; He our Rock, our hope of e - ter-nal sal-va-tion,
loud with ho-san-nas ring! Je - sus, Sav - ior, reigneth for-ev - er and ev - er;

Strength and hon - or give to His ho - ly name! Like a shep-herd, Je-sus will
Hail Him! hail Him! Je-sus the Cru - ci - fied. Sound His Praises! Je-sus who
Crown Him! crown Him! Prophet, and Priest, and King! Christ is com-ing! o-ver the

REFRAIN

guard His children, In His arms He carries them all day long:
bore our sorrows, Love unbounded, wonderful, deep and strong: Praise Him! praise Him!
world vic-to-rious, Pow'r and glo-ry un - to the Lord be-long:

tell of His ex-cel-lent greatness; Praise Him! praise Him! ev-er in joy-ful song!

81 AN EVENING PRAYER

C. M. Battersby
Arr. by C. H. G.

Chas. H. Gabriel

1. If I have wounded an - y soul to - day, If I have caused one foot to
2. If I have ut - tered i - dle words or vain, If I have turned a - side from
3. If I have been perverse, or hard or cold, If I have longed for shel - ter
4. For - give' the sins I have con - fessed to Thee; For - give the se - cret sins I

go a - stray, If I have walked in my own will - ful way, Dear Lord, for - give!
want or pain, Lest I of - fend some oth - er thru' the strain, Dear Lord, for - give!
in Thy fold, When Thou hast given me some fort to hold, Dear Lord, for - give!
do not see; O guide me, love me, and my keep - er be, ✗ ✗ ✗ ✗ A - men.

82 ONLY BELIEVE

P. R.

Paul Rader

CHORUS

On - ly be - lieve, on - ly be - lieve; All things are pos - si - ble, on - ly be - lieve;

On - ly be - lieve, on - ly be - lieve; All things are pos - si - ble, on - ly be - lieve.

83 NEAR TO THE HEART OF GOD

C. B. McAfee

1. There is a place of qui - et rest, Near to the heart of God,
2. There is a place of com - fort sweet, Near to the heart of God,
3. There is a place of full re - lease, Near to the heart of God,

A place where sin can - not mo - lest, Near to the heart of God.
A place where we our Sav - ior meet, Near to the heart of God.
A place where all is joy and peace, Near to the heart of God.

REFRAIN

O Je - sus, blest Re - deem - er, Sent from the heart of God,

Hold us, who wait be - fore Thee, Near to the heart of God.

84 THERE'S A WIDENESS IN GOD'S MERCY

Rev. F. W. Faber

Lizzie S. Tourjee

1. There's a wide-ness in God's mer-cy Like the wide-ness of the sea;
2. There is wel-come for the sin-ner, And more grac-es for the good;
3. For the love of God is broad-er Than the meas-ure of man's mind,
4. If our love were but more sim-ple, We should take Him at His word;

THERE'S A WIDENESS IN GOD'S MERGY

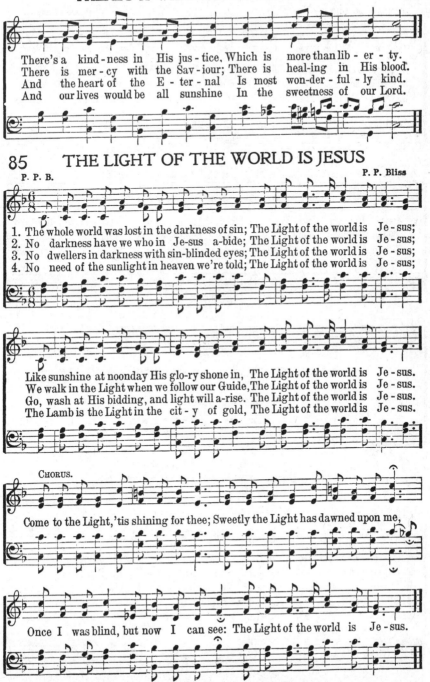

There's a kind-ness in His jus-tice, Which is more than lib - er - ty.
There is mer - cy with the Sav-iour; There is heal-ing in His blood.
And the heart of the E - ter - nal Is most won-der - ful - ly kind.
And our lives would be all sunshine In the sweetness of our Lord.

85   THE LIGHT OF THE WORLD IS JESUS

P. P. B.   P. P. Bliss

1. The whole world was lost in the darkness of sin; The Light of the world is Je-sus;
2. No darkness have we who in Je-sus a-bide; The Light of the world is Je-sus;
3. No dwellers in darkness with sin-blinded eyes; The Light of the world is Je-sus;
4. No need of the sunlight in heaven we're told; The Light of the world is Je-sus;

Like sunshine at noonday His glo-ry shone in, The Light of the world is Je-sus.
We walk in the Light when we follow our Guide, The Light of the world is Je-sus.
Go, wash at His bidding, and light will a-rise. The Light of the world is Je-sus.
The Lamb is the Light in the cit - y of gold, The Light of the world is Je-sus.

CHORUS.

Come to the Light, 'tis shining for thee; Sweetly the Light has dawned upon me,

Once I was blind, but now I can see: The Light of the world is Je-sus.

86   ROCK OF AGES

AUGUSTUS M. TOPLADY

THOMAS HASTINGS

1. Rock of A - ges, cleft for me, Let me hide my - self in Thee;
2. Could my tears for - ev - er flow, Could my zeal no lan-guor know,
3. While I draw this fleet - ing breath, When my eyes shall close in death,

Let the wa - ter and the blood, From Thy wound - ed side which flowed,
These for sin could not a - tone; Thou must save, and Thou a - lone:
When I rise to worlds unknown, And be - hold Thee on Thy throne,

Be of sin the dou - ble cure, Save from wrath and make me pure.
In my hand no price I bring, Sim - ply to Thy cross I cling.
Rock ot A - ges, cleft for me, Let me hide my - self in Thee.

87   NEARER, MY GOD, TO THEE

SARAH F. ADAMS

ARR. by LOWELL MASON

1. Near - er, my God, to Thee, Near - er to Thee! E'en though it
2. Though like the wan - der - er, The sun gone down, Dark - ness be
3. There let the way ap - pear, Steps un - to heav'n: All that Thou
4. Then, with my wak - ing tho'ts Bright with Thy praise, Out of my
5. Or if on - joy - ful wing, Cleav - ing the sky, Sun, moon, and

NEARER, MY GOD, TO THEE

be   a cross   That rais - eth   me;   Still all   my song shall be,
o - ver me,   My   rest   a   stone;   Yet in   my dreams I'd   be
send - est me,   In   mer - cy   giv'n: An - gels   to beck - on me,
sto - ny griefs   Beth - el I'll   raise;   So by   my woes to   be
stars for - got,   Up - wards I'll fly,   Still all   my song shall be,

Near - er, my God, to Thee, Near - er, my God, to Thee, Nearer, to Thee!

88 JESUS, LOVER OF MY SOUL

Charles Wesley

S. B. Marsh

FINE.

1. {Je - sus, Lov - er of my soul, Let me to Thy bos - om fly,
   {While the near - er wa - ters roll, While the tem-pest still is high!}
2. {Oth - er ref - uge have I none; Hangs my help-less soul on Thee:
   {Leave, ah, leave me not a - lone, Still sup-port and com - fort me!}
3. {Thou, O Christ, art all I want; More than all in Thee I find;
   {Raise the fall - en, cheer the faint, Heal the sick and lead the blind.}
4. {Plenteous grace with Thee is found, Grace to cov - er all my sin;
   {Let the heal-ing streams abound, Make and keep me pure with - in.}

D.C.-Safe in - to the ha - ven guide, O re - ceive my soul at last!
D.C.-Cov - er my de - fense-less head With the shad-ow of Thy wing.
D.C.-False and full of sin I am, Thou art full of truth and grace.
D.C.-Spring Thou up with-in my heart, Rise to all e - ter - ni - ty.

D. C.

Hide me, O my Sav - ior, hide, Till the storm of life is past;
All my trust on Thee is stayed, All my help from Thee I bring;
Just and ho - ly is Thy name, I am all un-right-eous - ness;
Thou of life the foun - tain art; Free-ly let me take of Thee;

89 SAVIOUR, THY DYING LOVE

S. D. Phelps

SOMETHING FOR JESUS

Robert Lowry

1. Sav - iour, Thy dy - ing love Thou gav - est me, Nor should I
2. At the blest mer - cy - seat, Plead-ing for me, My fee - ble
3. Give me a faith - ful heart,—Like-ness to Thee,— That each de -
4. All that I am and have,—Thy gifts so free,— In joy, in

aught with-hold, Dear Lord, from Thee: In love my soul would bow,
faith looks up, Je - sus, to Thee: Help me the cross to bear,
part - ing day Hence-forth may see Some work of love be - gun,
grief, thro' life, Dear Lord, for Thee! And when Thy face I see,

My heart ful - fill its vow, Some of-f'ring bring Thee now, Something for Thee.
Thy wondrous love declare, Some song to raise, or prayer, Something for Thee.
Some deed of kindness done, Some wand'rer sought and won, Something for Thee.
My ransomed soul shall be, Thro' all e - ter - ni - ty, Something for Thee.

90 I NEED THEE EVERY HOUR

Annie S. Hawks

Robert Lowry

1. I need Thee ev - 'ry hour, Most gra - cious Lord, No ten - der voice like
2. I need Thee ev - 'ry hour, Stay Thou near by; Temp-ta - tions lose their
3. I need Thee ev - 'ry hour, In joy or pain; Come quick-ly and a -
4. I need Thee ev - 'ry hour, Most Ho - ly One; Oh! make me Thine in -

I NEED THEE EVERY HOUR

REFRAIN

Thine Can peace af - ford.
pow'r When Thou art nigh.   I need Thee, O, I need Thee; Ev-'ry hour I
bide, Or life is vain.
deed, Thou bless-ed Son!

need Thee! O bless me now, my Sav - ior, I   come   to Thee!

91   O SAY, BUT I'M GLAD

(Dedicated to Bishop A. J. Moore)

COPYRIGHT, 1930, BY JAS. P. SULLIVAN
USED BY PERMISSION

Rev. James P. Sullivan   Mildred Ellen Sullivan

1. There is   a song in my heart to - day, Something I nev - er had;   Je - sus has
2. Won - der-ful, mar-vel-ous love He brings, In - to a heart that's sad;   Thru darkest
3. We have a fel - low-ship rich and sweet, Tongue can ne'er re - late;   Abid - ing in
4. Won't you come to Him with all your care, Wea-ry and worn and sad?   You, too, will

CHORUS

tak - en my sins a - way, O   say, but I'm glad!
tun-nels the soul just sings, O say, but I'm glad!   O say, but I'm glad, I'm glad,
Him is   a re - al treat, O   say, but it's great!
sing as His love you share, O say, but I'm glad!

O say, but I'm glad! Je-sus has come and my cup's o-ver-run, O say, but I'm glad!

92 ALL HAIL THE POWER OF JESUS' NAME

EDWARD PERRONET

OLIVER HOLDEN

1. All hail the pow'r of Je - sus' name, Let an - gels pros-trate fall;
2. Crown Him, ye morn-ing stars of light, Who fixed this earth - ly ball;
3. Sin - ners, whose love can ne'er for - get The worm-wood and the gall,
4. Let ev - 'ry kin - dred, ev - 'ry tribe On this ter - res-trial ball,
5. O that with yon - der sa - cred throng, We at His feet may fall;

Bring forth the roy - al di - a - dem, And crown Him Lord of all,
Now hail the strength of Israel's might, And crown Him Lord of all,
Go spread your tro-phies at His feet, And crown Him Lord of all,
To Him all maj - es - ty as-cribe, And crown Him Lord of all,
We'll join the ev - er - last-ing song, And crown Him Lord of all,

Bring forth the roy - al di - a - dem, And crown Him Lord of all.
Now hail the strength of Is-rael's might, And crown Him Lord of all.
Go, spread your tro-phies at His feet, And crown Him Lord of all.
To Him all maj - es - ty as-cribe, And crown Him Lord of all.
We'll join the ev - er - last-ing song, And crown Him Lord of all.

93 ON JORDAN'S STORMY BANKS

Samuel Stennett

Arr. by R. M. McIntosh

1. On Jor - dan's storm-y banks I stand, And cast a wish-ful eye
2. O'er all those wide-ex-tend-ed plains Shines one e - ter - nal day;
3. No chill - ing winds, nor pois'nous breath, Can reach that heath-ful shore;
4. When shall I reach that hap - py place, And be for - ev - er blest?

ON JORDAN'S STORMY BANKS

FINE

To Ca-naan's fair and hap-py land, Where my pos-ses-sions lie.
There God, the Son, for-ev-er reigns, And scat-ters night a-way.
Sick-ness and sor-row, pain and death, Are felt and feared no more.
When shall I see my Fa-ther's face, And in His bos-om rest?

D.S.—O who will come and go with me? I am bound for the prom-ised land.

REFRAIN

D. S.

I am bound for the promised land,.... I am bound for the promised land,
prom-ised land,

94   COME, THOU FOUNT

ROBERT ROBINSON

JOHN WYETH
FINE

1. { Come, Thou Fount of ev-'ry bless-ing, Tune my heart to sing Thy grace;
   { Streams of mer-cy, nev-er ceas-ing, Call for songs of loud-est praise. }
2. { Here I'll raise my Eb-en-e-zer, Hith-er by Thy help I'll come;
   { And I hope by Thy good pleasure, Safe-ly to ar-rive at home. }
3. { Oh, to grace how great a debt-or Dai-ly I'm constrained to be!
   { Let Thy goodness, like a fet-ter, Bind my wand'ring heart to Thee: }

D.C.—Praise the mount, I'm fixed up-on it! Mount of Thy re-deem-ing love.
D.C.—He, to res-cue me from dan-ger, In-ter-posed His pre-cious blood.
D.C.—Here's my heart, O take and seal it, Seal it for Thy courts a-bove.

D. C.

Teach me some mel-o-dious son-net, Sung by flam-ing tongues a-bove;
Je-sus sought me when a stranger, Wand'ring from the fold of God;
Prone to love Thee, Lord, I feel it, Prone to serve the God I love;

95 THE SAVIOR CAN SOLVE EVERY PROBLEM

Rev. Oswald J. Smith

B. D. Ackley

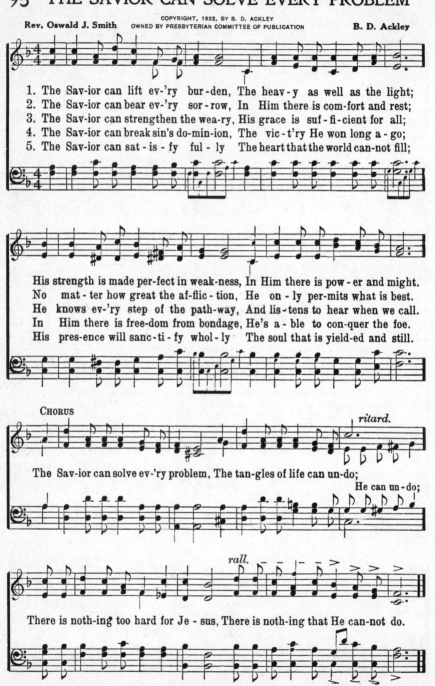

1. The Sav-ior can lift ev-'ry bur-den, The heav-y as well as the light;
2. The Sav-ior can bear ev-'ry sor-row, In Him there is com-fort and rest;
3. The Sav-ior can strengthen the wea-ry, His grace is suf-fi-cient for all;
4. The Sav-ior can break sin's do-min-ion, The vic-t'ry He won long a-go;
5. The Sav-ior can sat-is-fy ful-ly The heart that the world can-not fill;

His strength is made per-fect in weak-ness, In Him there is pow-er and might.
No mat-ter how great the af-flic-tion, He on-ly per-mits what is best.
He knows ev-'ry step of the path-way, And lis-tens to hear when we call.
In Him there is free-dom from bondage, He's a-ble to con-quer the foe.
His pres-ence will sanc-ti-fy whol-ly The soul that is yield-ed and still.

CHORUS

ritard.

The Sav-ior can solve ev-'ry problem, The tan-gles of life can un-do;

He can un-do;

rall.

There is noth-ing too hard for Je-sus, There is noth-ing that He can-not do.

96 FAIREST LORD JESUS

Crusaders' Hymn

Arr. by Richard S. Willis

1. Fair-est Lord Je - sus! Rul - er of all na - ture!
2. Fair are the mead - ows, Fair - er still the wood - lands,
3. Fair is the sun - shine, Fair - er still the moon - light,

O Thou of God and man the Son! Thee will I cher-ish,
Robed in the bloom-ing garb of spring; Je - sus is fair - er,
And all the twin - kling star - ry host; Je - sus shines bright-er,

Thee will I hon - or, Thou, my soul's glo - ry, joy, and crown!
Je - sus is pur - er, Who makes the woe - ful heart to sing!
Je - sus shines pur - er, Than all the an - gels heav'n can boast!

97 JESUS CALLS US

Mrs. Cecil F. Alexander

William H. Jude

1. Je - sus calls us; o'er the tu - mult Of our life's wild, rest-less sea,
2. Je - sus calls us from the wor - ship Of the vain world's gold-en store,
3. In our joys and in our sor - rows, Days of toil and hours of ease,
4. Je - sus calls us; by Thy mer - cies, Sav-ior, may we hear Thy call,

Day by day His sweet voice sound-eth, Say-ing, "Chris-tian, fol-low Me."
From each i - dol that would keep us, Say-ing, "Chris-tian, love Me more."
Still He calls, in cares and pleas-ures, "Christian, love Me more than these."
Give our hearts to Thy o - be-dience, Serve and love Thee best of all.

98 THE NAME OF JESUS

W. C. Martin

E. S. Lorenz

1. The name of Je - sus is so sweet, I love its mu - sic
2. I love the name of Him whose heart Knows all my griefs and
3. That name I fond - ly love to hear, It nev - er fails my
4. No word of man can ev - er tell How sweet the name I

to re - peat; It makes my joys full and com - plete, The pre - cious
bears a part; Who bids all an - xious fears de - part— I love the
heart to cheer, Its mu - sic dries the fall - ing tear; Ex - alt the
love so well, Oh, let its prais - es ev - er swell, Oh, praise the

CHORUS

name of Je - sus. "Je - sus," oh, how sweet the name!
pre - cious name,

"Je - sus," ev - 'ry day the same; "Je - sus," let all

saints pro - claim its wor - thy praise for - ev - er.
Its wor - thy praise

99 MAJESTIC SWEETNESS SITS ENTHRONED

Samuel Stennett ORTONVILLE C. M. Thomas Hastings

1. Majestic sweetness sits enthroned Upon the Saviour's brow; His head with radiant
2. He saw me plunged in deep distress, He flew to my relief; For me He bore the
3. To Him I owe my life and breath, And all the joys I have; He makes me triumph
4. To heav'n, the place of His abode, He brings my weary feet; Shows me the glories
5. Since from His bounty I receive Such proofs of love divine, Had I a thousand

glories crowned, His lips with grace o'erflow, His lips with grace o'erflow.
shameful cross, And carried all my grief, And carried all my grief.
o - ver death, He saves me from the grave, He saves me from the grave.
of my God, And makes my joys complete, And makes my joys complete.
hearts to give, Lord, they should all be Thine, Lord, they should all be Thine. A - men.

100 WE MAY NOT CLIMB THE HEAVENLY STEEPS

John G. Whittier SERENITY C. M. William V. Wallace

1. We may not climb the heav'n-ly steeps To bring the Lord Christ down;
2. But warm, sweet, ten-der e - ven yet A pres - ent help is He;
3. The heal - ing of His seam - less dress Is by our beds of pain;
4. Thro' Him the first fond pray'rs are said Our lips of child-hood frame;
5. O Lord and Mas-ter of us all, What-e'er our name or sign,

In vain we search the low - est deeps, For Him no depths can drown.
And faith has still its Ol - i - vet, And love its Gal - i - lee.
We touch Him in life's throng and press, And we are whole a-gain.
The last low whispers of our dead Are burdened with His name.
We own Thy sway, we hear Thy call, We test our lives by Thine! A - men.

101 'TIS MIDNIGHT; AND ON OLIVES' BROW

William B. Tappan   OLIVES' BROW L. M.   William B. Bradbury

1. 'Tis midnight; and on Ol-ive's brow The star is dimmed that late-ly shone:
2. 'Tis midnight; and from all re-moved The Sav-ior wrestles 'lone with fears;
3. 'Tis midnight; and for oth-ers' guilt The Man of Sor-rows weeps in blood;
4. 'Tis midnight; and from e-ther-plains Is borne the song that an-gels know;

'Tis midnight; in the gar-den now The suff'ring Sav-ior prays a-lone.
E'en that dis-ci-ple whom He loved Heeds not his Master's grief and tears.
Yet He that hath in an-guish knelt Is not for-sak-en by His God.
Un-heard by mor-tals are the strains That sweetly soothe the Sav-ior's woe.

102 REJOICE, YE PURE IN HEART

Edward A. Plumptre   Arthur H. Messiter

1. Re - joice, ye pure in heart, Re - joice, give thanks and sing;
2. Bright youth and snow-crowned age, Strong men and maid-ens fair,
3. Yes, on thru life's long path, Still chant-ing as ye go;
4. Still lift your stand-ard high, Still march in firm ar - ray,

Your fes - tal ban-ner wave on high,—The cross of Christ your King.
Raise high your free, ex-ult-ing song, God's wondrous praise de-clare.
From youth to age, by night and day, In glad-ness and in woe.
As war-riors thru the dark-ness toil, Till dawns the gold-en day.

REFRAIN

Re-joice, re-joice, Re-joice, give thanks and sing! A-MEN.
Re-joice, re-joice,

103   PRAISE HIS NAME

C. H. G.   Chas. H. Gabriel

1. All the way my Lord is lead-ing me, Praise His name, Praise His name!
2. When I faint, His grace up-hold-eth me; Praise His name, Praise His name!
3. Cares of life have o-ver-tak-en me; Praise His name, Praise His name!
Praise............ His name!

With His heav'nly man-na feed-ing me, Praise His ho-ly name.
When I fear, His arms en-fold-eth me, Praise His ho-ly name.
Yet He nev-er has for-sak-en me, Praise His ho-ly name.
Praise His name.

REFRAIN.

Je-sus, Je-sus! This is my song, Je-sus, Je-sus, the whole day long;

He is mine, A Sav-ior di-vine,—Praise His ho-ly name.
Praise His name.

104 O THOU IN WHOSE PRESENCE

Joseph Swain

Freeman Lewis

1. O Thou in whose pres - ence my soul takes de - light, On
2. Where dost Thou, dear Shep - herd, re - sort with Thy sheep, To
3. O why should I wan - der an a - lien from Thee, Or
4. Ye daughters of Zi - on, de - clare, have you seen The

whom in af - flic - tion I call, My com - fort by day, and my
feed them in pas - tures of love? Say, why in the val - ley of
cry in the des - ert for bread? Thy foes will re - joice when my
star that on Is - ra - el shone? Say, if in your tents my Be -

song in the night, My hope, my sal - va - tion, my all!
death should I weep, Or a - lone in this wil - der - ness rove?
sor - rows they see, And smile at the tears I have shed.
lov - ed has been, And where with His flocks He is gone.

105 JESUS, SAVIOR, PILOT ME

Edward Hopper

J. E. Gould

FINE.

1. Je - sus, Sav - ior, pi - lot me O - ver life's tem-pes-tuous sea;
D.C.—Chart and com - pass come from Thee, Je - sus, Sav - ior, pi - lot me.
2. As a moth - er stills her child, Thou canst hush the o-cean wild.
D.C.—Wondrous Sov-'reign of the sea; Je - sus, Sav - ior, pi - lot me.
3. When at last I near the shore, And the fear - ful breakers roar,
D.C.—May I hear Thee say to me; "Fear not, I will pi - lot thee."

JESUS, SAVIOR, PILOT ME

Un-known waves a-round me roll, Hid - ing rocks and treach'rous shoal;
Boist'rous waves o - bey Thy will When Thou say'st to them be still!"
'Twixt me and the peaceful rest, Then, while lean-ing on Thy breast,

106   I WOULD BE TRUE

HOWARD ARNOLD WALTER   JOSEPH YATES PEEK

1. I would be true, for there are those who trust me; I would be
2. I would be friend of all— the foe, the friend-less; I would be

pure, for there are those who care;   I would be strong, for
giv - 'ing, and for-get the gift;   I would be hum - ble,

there is much to suf - fer;   I would be brave, for there is much to
for I know my weak-ness;   I would look up, and laugh, and love, and

dare,   I would be brave,   for there is much to dare.
lift,   I would look up,   and laugh, and love, and lift.

107 JESUS, ROSE OF SHARON

Ida A. Guirey   Chas. H. Gabriel

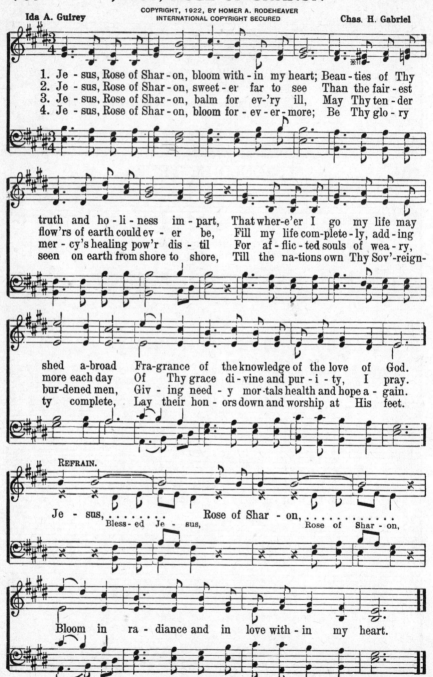

1. Je - sus, Rose of Shar - on, bloom with - in my heart; Beau - ties of Thy
2. Je - sus, Rose of Shar - on, sweet - er far to see Than the fair - est
3. Je - sus, Rose of Shar - on, balm for ev - 'ry ill, May Thy ten - der
4. Je - sus, Rose of Shar - on, bloom for - ev - er - more; Be Thy glo - ry

truth and ho - li - ness im - part, That wher-e'er I go my life may
flow'rs of earth could ev - er be, Fill my life com-plete - ly, add - ing
mer - cy's healing pow'r dis - til For af - flic - ted souls of wea - ry,
seen on earth from shore to shore, Till the na-tions own Thy Sov'-reign-

shed a-broad Fra-grance of the knowledge of the love of God.
more each day Of Thy grace di - vine and pur - i - ty, I pray.
bur-dened men, Giv - ing need - y mor-tals health and hope a - gain.
ty complete, Lay their hon - ors down and worship at His feet.

REFRAIN.

Je - sus, ... Rose of Shar - on, ...
   Bless - ed Je - sus,   Rose of Shar - on,

Bloom in ra - diance and in love with - in my heart.

108 PRAYER IS THE SOUL'S SINCERE DESIRE

James Montgomery   LAMBETH C. M.   Anonymous

1. Pray'r is the soul's sin-cere de-sire, Ut-tered or un - ex - pressed;
2. Pray'r is the bur - den of a sigh, The fall-ing of a tear,
3. Pray'r is the sim - plest form of speech That in-fant lips can try;
4. Pray'r is the con - trite sinner's voice, Re-turn-ing from his ways;
5. Pray'r is the Chris-tian's vi - tal breath, The Christian's na - tive air,
6. O Thou, by whom we come to God, The Life, the Truth, the Way;

The mo-tion of a hid-den fire That trembles in the breast.
The upward glanc-ing of an eye, When none but God is near.
Pray'r the sub - lim-est strains that reach The Maj-es - ty on high.
While an-gels in their songs re-joice And cry, "Be-hold, he prays!"
His watchword at the gates of death; He en-ters heav'n with pray'r.
The path of pray'r Thyself hast trod: Lord, teach us how to pray! A - men.

109 MY SOUL, BE ON THY GUARD

George Heath   LABAN S. M.   Lowell Mason

1. My soul, be on thy guard; Ten thous-and foes a - rise;
2. Oh! watch, and fight, and pray; The bat - tle ne'er give o'er;
3. Ne'er think the vic - t'ry won, Nor lay thine ar - mor down;
4. Fight on, my soul, till death Shall bring thee to thy God;

The hosts of sin are press - ing hard To draw thee from the skies.
Re - new it bold-ly ev - 'ry day, And help di-vine im-plore.
The work of faith will not be done, Till thou ob-tain the crown.
He'll take thee, at thy part - ing breath, To His di-vine a - bode. A - men.

110 JESUS IS ALWAYS THERE

B. M. L.

Bertha Mae Lillenas

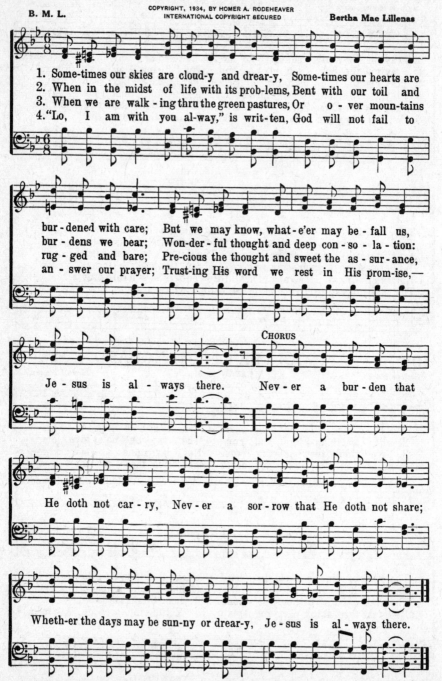

1. Some-times our skies are cloud-y and drear-y, Some-times our hearts are
2. When in the midst of life with its prob-lems, Bent with our toil and
3. When we are walk-ing thru the green pastures, Or o-ver moun-tains
4. "Lo, I am with you al-way," is writ-ten, God will not fail to

bur-dened with care; But we may know, what-e'er may be-fall us,
bur-dens we bear; Won-der-ful thought and deep con-so-la-tion:
rug-ged and bare; Pre-cious the thought and sweet the as-sur-ance,
an-swer our prayer; Trust-ing His word we rest in His prom-ise,—

Chorus

Je-sus is al-ways there. Nev-er a bur-den that

He doth not car-ry, Nev-er a sor-row that He doth not share;

Wheth-er the days may be sun-ny or drear-y, Je-sus is al-ways there.

111　O FOR A THOUSAND TONGUES

AZMON

CHARLES WESLEY

CARL G. GLASER
Arr. by LOWELL MASON

1. O   for a thou - sand tongues to sing   My great Re-deem - er's praise,
2. My   gracious Mas - ter and my God, As - sist me to   pro - claim,
3. Je - sus! the name that charms our fears, That bids our sor - rows cease;
4. He breaks the pow'r of   canceled sin, He sets the pris - 'ner free;
5. Hear Him, ye deaf; His praise, ye dumb, Your loosened tongues em - ploy;

The glo-ries of   my   God and King,   The triumphs of   His grace.
To spread thro' all   the   earth a-broad The hon-ors of   Thy name.
'Tis mu - sic in   the   sin-ner's ears, 'Tis life, and health, and peace.
His blood can make the   foul - est clean; His blood a-vailed for   me.
Ye   blind, be-hold your Sav - ior come; And leap, ye lame, for joy.

112　DEAR LORD AND FATHER OF MANKIND

John G. Whittier

ELTON 8. 6. 8. 8. 6.

Frederick C. Maker

1. Dear Lord and Father of mankind, Forgive our fev'rish ways! Reclothe us in our
2. In simple trust, like theirs who heard, Beside the Syrian sea, The gracious calling
3. O   Sabbath rest by Gal - i -lee! O calm of hills a-bove, Where Jesus knelt to
4. Drop Thy still dews of qui-et-ness, Till all our strivings cease; Take from our souls the
5. Breathe thro' the heats of our desire Thy coolness and Thy balm; Let sense be dumb, let

rightful mind; In pur-er lives Thy serv-ice find, In deeper rev'rence, praise.
of   the Lord, Let us, like them, without a word, Rise up and fol-low Thee.
share with Thee The silence of e - ter - ni - ty, In - ter-pret-ed by love!
strain and stress, And let our ordered lives confess The beauty of Thy peace.
flesh retire: Speak thro' the earthquake, wind and fire, O still small voice of calm! A-men.

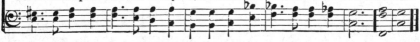

113 TRUE-HEARTED, WHOLE-HEARTED

Frances R. Havergal

George C. Stebbins

1. True-hearted, whole-hearted, faith-ful and loy-al, King of our lives, by Thy
2. True-hearted, whole-hearted, full-est al-le-giance, Yielding henceforth to our
3. True-hearted, whole-hearted, Sav-ior all-glo-rious! Take Thy great pow-er and

grace we will be; Un-der the stan-dard ex-alt-ed and roy-al,
glo-ri-ous King; Val-iant en-deav-or and lov-ing o-be-dience
reign there a-lone, O-ver our wills and af-fec-tions vic-to-rious,

CHORUS

Strong in Thy strength we will bat-tle for Thee. Peal out the watchword!
Free-ly and joy-ous-ly now we would bring.
Free-ly sur-ren-dered and whol-ly Thine own. Peal

si-lence it nev-er, Song of our spir-its re-joic-ing and free; Peal out the
si-lence Song re-joic-ing and free; Peal

watch-word! loy-al for-ev-er, King of our lives, by Thy grace we will be.
loy-al King

O JESUS, THOU ART STANDING

WILLIAM W. HOW

JUSTIN H. KNECHT

1. O Je - sus, Thou art stand - ing Out - side the fast-closed door,
2. O Je - sus, Thou art knock - ing; And lo, that hand is scarred,
3. O Je - sus, Thou art plead - ing In ac - cents meek and low,

In low - ly pa - tience wait - ing To pass the thresh - old o'er:
And thorns Thy brow en - cir - cle, And tears Thy face have marred:
"I died for you, my chil - dren, And will you treat Me so?"

Shame on us, Chris-tian broth - ers, His name and sign who bear,
O love that pass - eth knowl - edge, So pa - tient - ly to wait!
O Lord, with shame and sor - row We o - pen now the door;

O shame, thrice shame up - on us, To keep Him stand - ing there!
O sin that hath no e - qual, So fast to bar the gate!
Dear Sav - ior, en - ter, en - ter, And leave us nev - er - more.

115 I AM THINE, O LORD

Fanny J. Crosby

W. H. Doane

1. I am Thine, O Lord, I have heard Thy voice, And it
2. Con - se - crate me now to Thy serv - ice, Lord, By the
3. O the pure de - light of a sin - gle hour That be -
4. There are depths of love that I can - not know Till I

told Thy love to me; But I long to rise in the arms of faith,
pow'r of grace di - vine; Let my soul look up with a stead-fast hope,
fore Thy throne I spend, When I kneel in prayer, and with Thee, my God,
cross the nar - row sea; There are heights of joy that I may not reach

And be clos - er drawn to Thee.
And my will be lost in Thine.
I com-mune as friend with friend!
Till I rest in peace with Thee.

REFRAIN

Draw me near - er,
near - er, near - er,

near - er, bless-ed Lord, To the cross where Thou hast died; Draw me

near - er, near - er, near - er, bless-ed Lord, To Thy precious, bleed-ing side.

116 OUR BEST

S. C. Kirk

Grant Colfax Tullar

With dignity

1. Hear ye the Mas-ter's call, "Give Me thy best!" For, be it great or small,
2. Wait not for men to laud, Heed not their slight; Win-ning the smile of God
3. Night soon comes on a-pace, Day has-tens by; Workman and work must face

That is His test. Do then the best you can, Not for re-ward, Not for the
Brings its de-light! Aid-ing the good and true Ne'er goes un-blest, All that we
Test-ing on high. Oh, may we in that day Find rest, sweet rest, Which God has

CHORUS

praise of man, But for the Lord.
think or do, Be it the best.   Ev-'ry work for Je-sus will be blest,
promised those Who do their best.

But He asks from ev-'ry-one his best. Our tal-ents may be few,

These may be small, But un-to Him is due Our best, our all.

SOUND THE BATTLE CRY

W. F. S.

WM. F. SHERWIN

1. Sound the bat-tle cry! See, the foe is nigh; Raise the standard high
2. Strong to meet the foe, Marching on we go, While our cause we know,
3. O! Thou God of all, Hear us when we call, Help us one and all

For the Lord; Gird your ar-mor on, Stand firm, ev-'ry one; Rest your
Must pre-vail; Shield and banner bright, Gleam-ing in the light; Bat-tling
By Thy grace; When the bat-tle's done, And the vic-t'ry's won, May we

CHORUS ff

cause up-on His ho-ly word.
for the right We ne'er can fail. Rouse, then, sol-diers, ral-ly round the
wear the crown Be-fore Thy face.

ban-ner, Read-y, stead-y, pass the word a-long; Onward, for-ward,

shout a-loud Ho-san-na! Christ is Cap-tain of the might-y throng.

ONWARD, CHRISTIAN SOLDIERS

Sabine Baring-Gould

Arthur Sullivan

1. On-ward, Christian sol - diers! Marching as to war, With the cross of
2. Like a might - y ar - my Moves the Church of God; Brothers, we are
3. Crowns and thrones may perish, Kingdoms rise and wane; But the Church of
4. On-ward, then, ye peo - ple! Join our happy throng; Blend with ours your

Je - sus Go - ing on be - fore; Christ, the roy - al Mas - ter,
tread - ing Where the saints have trod; We are not di - vid - ed,
Je - sus Con-stant will re - main; Gates of hell can nev - er
voic - es In the tri-umph song; Glo - ry, laud, and hon - or,

Leads a-gainst the foe; For-ward in - to bat - tle, See, His banners go!
All one bod - y we; One in hope and doc - trine, One in char - i - ty.
'Gainst that Church prevail; We have Christ's own promise, Which can never fail.
Un - to Christ the King; This thro' countless a - ges Men and an - gels sing.

CHORUS

On-ward, Chris-tian sol - diers! March-ing as to war,

With the cross of Je - sus Go - ing on be - fore.

119   MY REDEEMER

P. P. BLISS   JAMES McGRANAHAN

1. I will sing of my Re-deem-er, And His won-drous love to me;
2. I will tell the won-drous sto-ry, How my lost es-tate to save,
3. I will praise my dear Re-deem-er, His tri-um-phant pow'r I'll tell,
4. I will sing of my Re-deem-er, And His heav'n-ly love to me;

On the cru-el cross He suf-fered, From the curse to set me free.
In His bound-less love and mer-cy, He the ran-som free-ly gave.
How the vic-to-ry He giv-eth O-ver sin, and death, and hell.
He from death to life hath bro't me, Son of God with Him to be.

CHORUS

Sing, oh, sing . . . . . . of my Re-deem-er,
of my Re-deem-er, Sing, oh, sing of my Re-deem-er,

With His blood . . . . He pur-chased me, ...
He pur-chased me, With His blood He pur-chased me,

On the cross . . . . He sealed my par-don,
He sealed my par-don, On the cross He sealed my par-don,

MY REDEEMER

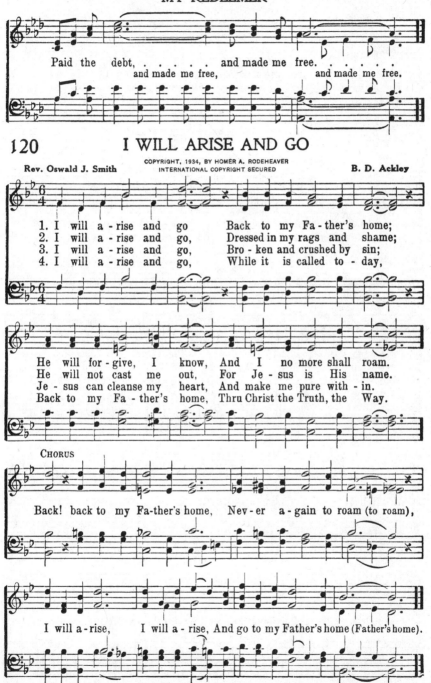

Paid the debt, ... and made me free. . . . . .
and made me free,   and made me free.

120   I WILL ARISE AND GO

COPYRIGHT, 1934, BY HOMER A. RODEHEAVER
INTERNATIONAL COPYRIGHT SECURED

Rev. Oswald J. Smith   B. D. Ackley

1. I will a-rise and go   Back to my Fa-ther's home;
2. I will a-rise and go,   Dressed in my rags and shame;
3. I will a-rise and go,   Bro-ken and crushed by sin;
4. I will a-rise and go,   While it is called to-day,

He will for-give, I know, And I no more shall roam.
He will not cast me out, For Je-sus is His name.
Je-sus can cleanse my heart, And make me pure with-in.
Back to my Fa-ther's home, Thru Christ the Truth, the Way.

CHORUS

Back! back to my Fa-ther's home, Nev-er a-gain to roam (to roam),

I will a-rise, I will a-rise, And go to my Father's home (Father's home).

THE FIGHT IS ON

Mrs. C. H. M.   Mrs. C. H. Morris

1. The fight is on, the trump-et sound is ring-ing out, The cry "To
2. The fight is on, a-rouse, ye sol-diers brave and true! Je - ho - vah
3. The Lord is lead-ing on to cer-tain vic-to-ry; The bow of

arms!" is heard a-far and near; The Lord of hosts is march-ing on to
leads, and vic-t'ry will as-sure; Go buck-le on the ar-mor God has
prom-ise spans the east-ern sky; His glo-rious name in ev - 'ry land shall

vic - to - ry, The tri - umph of the Christ will soon ap - pear.
giv - en you, And in His strength un - to the end en - dure.
hon - ored be; The morn will break, the dawn of peace is nigh.

CHORUS *Unison*

The fight is on, O Chris-tian sol - dier, And face to face in stern ar - ray, .. With

ar-mor gleaming, and col-ors streaming, The right and wrong engage to-day!

THE FIGHT IS ON

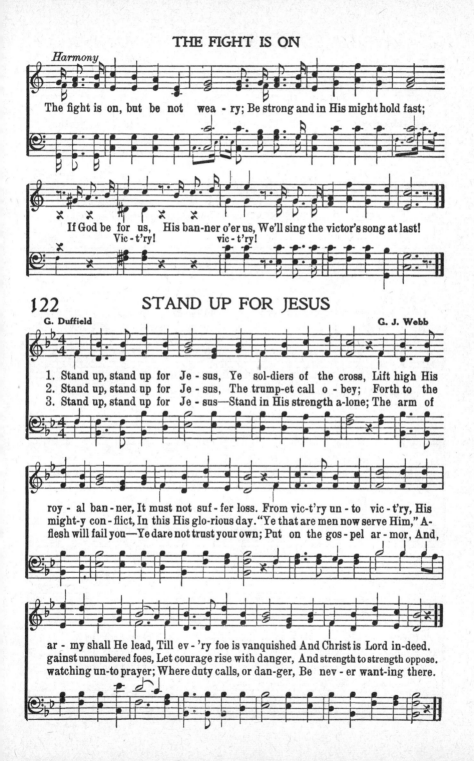

Harmony

The fight is on, but be not wea-ry; Be strong and in His might hold fast;

If God be for us, His ban-ner o'er us, We'll sing the victor's song at last!
Vic-t'ry! vic-t'ry!

122 STAND UP FOR JESUS

G. Duffield

G. J. Webb

1. Stand up, stand up for Je-sus, Ye sol-diers of the cross, Lift high His
2. Stand up, stand up for Je-sus, The trump-et call o-bey; Forth to the
3. Stand up, stand up for Je-sus—Stand in His strength a-lone; The arm of

roy-al ban-ner, It must not suf-fer loss. From vic-t'ry un-to vic-t'ry, His
might-y con-flict, In this His glo-rious day. "Ye that are men now serve Him," A-
flesh will fail you—Ye dare not trust your own; Put on the gos-pel ar-mor, And,

ar-my shall He lead, Till ev-'ry foe is vanquished And Christ is Lord in-deed.
gainst unnumbered foes, Let courage rise with danger, And strength to strength oppose.
watching un-to prayer; Where duty calls, or dan-ger, Be nev-er want-ing there.

123 GIVE OF YOUR BEST TO THE MASTER

H. B. G.

Mrs. Charles Barnard

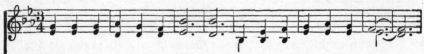

1. Give of your best to the Mas - ter; Give of the strength of your youth;
2. Give of your best to the Mas - ter; Give Him first place in your heart;
3. Give of your best to the Mas - ter; Naught else is worth-y His love;

Ref.—*Give of your best to the Mas - ter; Give of the strength of your youth;*

FINE

Throw your soul's fresh, glowing ar - dor In - to the bat - tle for truth.
Give Him first place in your serv - ice, Con - se-crate ev - 'ry part.
He gave Him-self for your ran - som, Gave up His glo - ry a - bove:

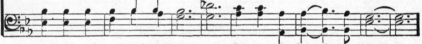

Clad in sal - va-tion's full arm - or, Join in the bat - tle for truth.

Je - sus has set the ex - am - ple; Dauntless was He, young and brave;
Give, and to you shall be giv - en; God His be - lov - ed Son gave;
Laid down His life with-out mur - mur, You from sin's ru-in to save;

rall. D. C.

Give Him your loy-al de - vo - tion, Give Him the best that you have.....
Grate-ful-ly seeking to serve Him, Give Him the best that you have.....
Give Him your heart's ad-o-ra - tion, Give Him the best that you have.....

124   LEAD ON, O KING ETERNAL

ERNEST W. SHURTLEFF   LANCASHIRE   HENRY SMART

1. Lead on, O King E - ter - nal, The day of march has come;
2. Lead on, O King E - ter - nal, Till sin's fierce war shall cease,
3. Lead on, O King E - ter - nal, We fol - low, not with fears;

Henceforth in fields of con - quest Thy tents shall be our home.
And ho - li - ness shall whis - per The sweet A - men of peace;
For glad-ness breaks like morn - ing Wher-e'er Thy face ap - pears;

Thro' days of prep - a - ra - tion Thy grace has made us strong,
For not with swords loud clash-ing, Nor roll of stir - ring drums;
Thy cross is lift - ed o'er us; We jour - ney in its light:

And now, O King e - ter - nal, We lift our bat - tle song.
With deeds of love and mer - cy, The heav'n-ly king - dom comes.
The crown a - waits the con - quest; Lead on, O God of might.

FORWARD THROUGH THE AGES

Frederick L. Hosmer

Arthur S. Sullivan

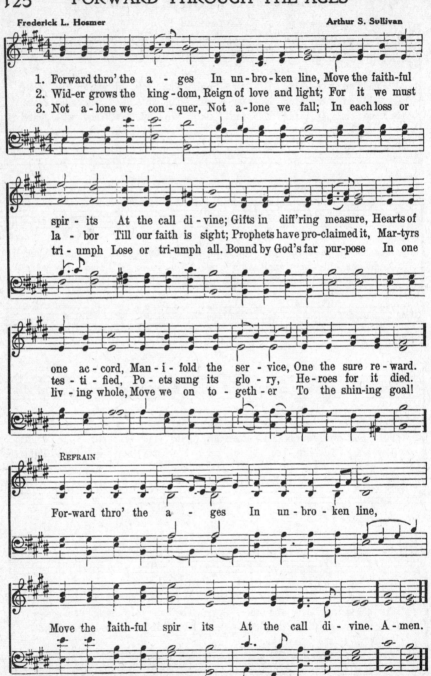

1. Forward thro' the a - ges In un-bro-ken line, Move the faith-ful
2. Wid-er grows the king-dom, Reign of love and light; For it we must
3. Not a-lone we con - quer, Not a-lone we fall; In each loss or

spir - its At the call di - vine; Gifts in diff'ring measure, Hearts of
la - bor Till our faith is sight; Prophets have pro-claimed it, Mar-tyrs
tri - umph Lose or tri-umph all. Bound by God's far pur-pose In one

one ac - cord, Man - i - fold the ser - vice, One the sure re - ward.
tes - ti - fied, Po - ets sung its glo - ry, He - roes for it died.
liv - ing whole, Move we on to - geth - er To the shin-ing goal!

REFRAIN

For-ward thro' the a - ges In un-bro - ken line,

Move the faith-ful spir - its At the call di - vine. A - men.

126 THE SON OF GOD GOES FORTH TO WAR

Reginald Heber ALL SAINTS C. M. D. Henry S. Cutler

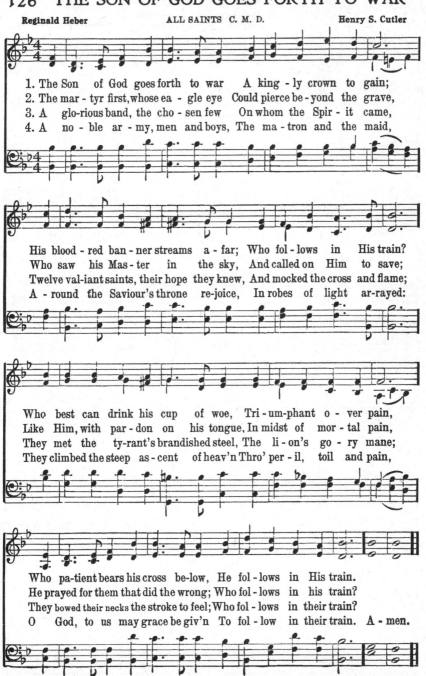

1. The Son of God goes forth to war A king - ly crown to gain;
2. The mar - tyr first, whose ea - gle eye Could pierce be - yond the grave,
3. A glo-rious band, the cho - sen few On whom the Spir - it came,
4. A no - ble ar - my, men and boys, The ma - tron and the maid,

His blood - red ban - ner streams a - far; Who fol - lows in His train?
Who saw his Mas - ter in the sky, And called on Him to save;
Twelve val-iant saints, their hope they knew, And mocked the cross and flame;
A - round the Saviour's throne re-joice, In robes of light ar-rayed:

Who best can drink his cup of woe, Tri - um-phant o - ver pain,
Like Him, with par - don on his tongue, In midst of mor - tal pain,
They met the ty-rant's brandished steel, The li - on's go - ry mane;
They climbed the steep as - cent of heav'n Thro' per - il, toil and pain,

Who pa-tient bears his cross be-low, He fol - lows in His train.
He prayed for them that did the wrong; Who fol - lows in his train?
They bowed their necks the stroke to feel; Who fol - lows in their train?
O God, to us may grace be giv'n To fol - low in their train. A - men.

127 THE VICTORY IS NIGH

B. M. L.

Bertha Mae Lillenas

1. March on, march on, ye sol-diers of the cross, The vic-t'ry soon will be won (will be won);
2. March on, march on, with banners bright unfurled, The vic-t'ry soon will be won (will be won);
3. March on, march on, King Je-sus leads the way, The vic-t'ry soon will be won (will be won);

March on, march on, nor shall we suf-fer loss, The vic-to-ry is nigh!
March on, march on, and tell to all the world The vic-to-ry is nigh!
March on, march on, be-hold the break-ing day, The vic-to-ry is nigh!

CHORUS *Unison*

March on, march on, O church of God, The vic-t'ry shout-ing, The foes we're

rout-ing! March on, march on, O church of God, With ban-ners lift-ed high;

Parts

This glo-rious tri-umph is just be-gun, The day of vic-to-ry is

THE VICTORY IS NIGH

al-most won; March on, march on, O church of God, The vic-to-ry is nigh!

128 JESUS MEANS EVERYTHING TO ME

Leonard Cecil Barnett

COPYRIGHT, 1934, BY HOMER A. RODEHEAVER
INTERNATIONAL COPYRIGHT SECURED

Harry Dixon Loes

1. Ere I sought di-vine con-trol, Life was ne'er from long-ing free;
2. Earth-ly pleas-ures draw no more, Well I know they soon shall end.
3. Wis-dom, cour-age, grace are mine, As I live by faith and prayer;

But since Je-sus saved my soul, He means ev-'ry-thing to me.
Joys are mine in boun-teous store, As my life for God I spend.
Naught my peace can un-der-mine, He will ev-'ry bur-den share.

CHORUS

Je-sus means ev-'ry-thing to me, Sav-ior, my on-ly hope is He,

For time and for e-ter-ni-ty— He means ev-'ry-thing to me.

129 AT THE BATTLE'S FRONT

Mrs. C. H. M.

COPYRIGHT, 1934, RENEWAL
HOMER A. RODEHEAVER, OWNER

Mrs. C. H. Morris

1. I've en-list-ed for life in the ar-my of the Lord, Tho' the
2. With the ban-ner of love and of ho-li-ness un-furled, Full sal-
3. Is your name, friend, en-rolled with the loy-al ones and true? Will you

fight may be long and the struggle fierce and hard; With the ar-mor of God
va-tion pro-claim to a sin-ful, dy-ing world; Tho' the darts thick and fast
dare now to stand with the Sav-ior's faith-ful few? Will you join with me now

and the Spir-it's trust-y sword, At the front of the bat-tle you will find me.
from the en-e-my be hurled, At the front of the bat-tle you will find me.
and the cov-e-nant re-new? At the front of the bat-tle you will find me.

CHORUS

Hear the tramp! tramp! tramping of the ar - my, The triumph shouting, the foe we're
Tramp! tramp! tramp! tramp! tramp! tramp! Tramp! tramp! tramp!

rout - ing; Hear the tramp! tramp! tramping of the ar - my, March-ing
tramp! tramp! tramp! Tramp! tramp! tramp! tramp! tramp! tramp!

AT THE BATTLE'S FRONT

on to vic-to-ry, ... I'm in this ar-my, this glo-rious
hal-le-lu - jah! Tramp! tramp! tramp!

ar - my, And the God of bat-tles will de-fend me; I'm in this
tramp! tramp! tramp!

ar - my, this glorious ar-my, At the front of the bat-tle you will find me.
Tramp! tramp! tramp!   tramp! tramp! tramp!

130 FIGHT THE GOOD FIGHT

John S. B. Monsell

William Boyd

1. Fight the good fight with all thy might, Christ is thy strength, and Christ thy right;
2. Run the straight race thru God's good grace, Lift up thine eyes, and seek His face;
3. Cast care a-side, lean on thy Guide; His boundless mer-cy will pro-vide;
4. Faint not, nor fear, His arms are near; He changeth not, and thou art dear;

Lay hold on life, and it shall be Thy joy and crown e-ter-nal-ly.
Life with its way be-fore us lies, Christ is the path, and Christ the prize.
Trust, and thy trust-ing soul shall prove Christ is its life, and Christ its love.
On-ly be-lieve, and thou shalt see That Christ is all in all to thee.

131 MARCHING WITH THE HEROES

William George Tarrant

Adam Geibel

Unison

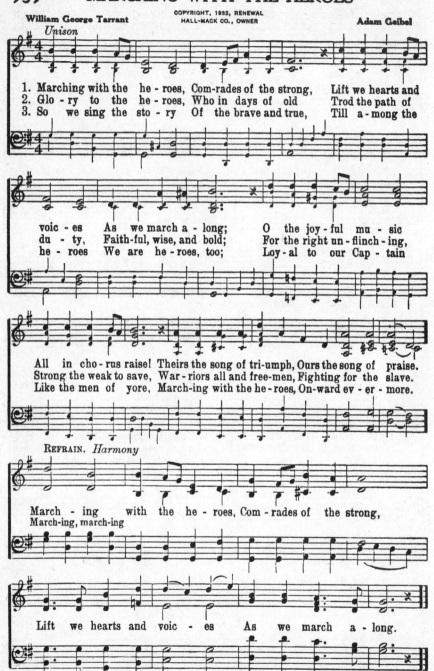

1. Marching with the he - roes, Com-rades of the strong, Lift we hearts and
2. Glo - ry to the he - roes, Who in days of old Trod the path of
3. So we sing the sto - ry Of the brave and true, Till a - mong the

voic - es As we march a - long; O the joy - ful mu - sic
du - ty, Faith-ful, wise, and bold; For the right un - flinch - ing,
he - roes We are he - roes, too; Loy - al to our Cap - tain

All in cho - rus raise! Theirs the song of tri-umph, Ours the song of praise.
Strong the weak to save, War - riors all and free-men, Fighting for the slave.
Like the men of yore, March-ing with the he - roes, On-ward ev - er - more.

REFRAIN. *Harmony*

March - ing with the he - roes, Com - rades of the strong,
March-ing, march-ing

Lift we hearts and voic - es As we march a - long.

132   IN THE SERVICE OF THE KING

A. H. Ackley

B. D. Ackley

1. I am hap-py in the serv-ice of the King, I am hap-py
2. I am hap-py in the serv-ice of the King, I am hap-py
3. I am hap-py in the serv-ice of the King, I am hap-py
4. I am hap-py in the serv-ice of the King, I am hap-py

Oh, so hap-py; I have peace and joy that noth-ing else can bring,
Oh, so hap-py; Thro' the sun-shine and the shad-ow I can sing,
Oh, so hap-py; To His guid-ing hand for-ev-er I will cling,
Oh, so hap-py; All that I pos-sess to Him I glad-ly bring,

In the serv-ice of the King.

REFRAIN.

In the serv-ice of the King Ev-'ry tal-ent I will bring; I have peace and joy and bless-ing In the serv-ice of the King.

133 SOLDIERS OF THE CROSS, ARISE

Rev. A. H. Ackley

B. D. Ackley

1. Sol - diers of the Cross, a - rise! The clar - ion call to arms is heard;
2. Sol - diers of the Cross, a - rise! The King of Right-eous-ness commands;
3. Sol - diers of the Cross, a - rise! In val-iant deeds in-scribe your name,

Hark to the need of hu - man cries, And let your soul with might be gird.
Be - hold His char-iots in the skies, The vic - to - ry is in His hands.
Not on the scroll of world-ly wise, But on God's no - ble roll of fame.

Thro' all the world the bat - tle wage, Till tyr - an - ny shall quake and flee.
'Tis you He sum-mons, "Fol-low Me" In - to the fray, nor fear to tread
Fight on with pa-tience that en-dures, Nor fal - ter till the day is done;

rall.

And there shall dawn the Gold-en Age, That long ex - pect-ed day to be.
The path of faith, and you shall see The world a - ris - en from the dead.
The crown-ing shall at last be yours, Of hav-ing fought and hav-ing won.

CHORUS

Sol-diers of the Cross, a - rise, a - rise, Our God is lead-ing, He sup-plies

The ar-mor of His might; O heed His call, a-rise, a-way, For

vic-to-ry is yours to-day! O Sol-diers of the Cross, a-rise, O

Sol-diers of the Cross, a-rise, O Sol-diers of the Cross, a-rise!

a-rise!

134 I CHOOSE JESUS

COPYRIGHT, 1934, BY HOMER A. RODEHEAVER
INTERNATIONAL COPYRIGHT SECURED

Rev. Oswald J. Smith   B. D. Ackley

1. I choose Je-sus, the Man of Gal-i-lee, Choose Him as my Friend;
2. I choose Je-sus, the Christ of Cal-va-ry, He who died for me;
3. I choose Je-sus, the Hope of all the world, At His feet I bow;

rall.

He will keep me day by day, He will keep me—Keep me to the end.
I am His, and His a-lone— I choose Je-sus—for e-ter-ni-ty.
As my Sav-ior, Lord and King, I choose Je-sus— I choose Je-sus now.

135 FORWARD

A. H. A.   Rev. A. H. Ackley

1. Lo, the Land of Prom-ise lies be-fore us, Filled with blessings for our
2. Though by might-y foes we are surround-ed, We will meet them with a
3. He will help us in each true en-deav-or, As to Him the lost we

hearts to claim, See the ban-ner of His cross is o'er us,
cour-age strong, He who leads us can-not be con-found-ed,
seek to bring; Grant to us the crown of life for-ev-er,

CHORUS

Let us en-ter in the Sav-iour's name. ⎫
Strength and vic-to-ry to Him be-long. ⎬ For-ward, for-ward,
For our loy-al-ty to Christ the King. ⎭

be our watchword, Forward, forward, 'tis the Lord's command; God de-fends us,

an-y-where He sends us, For-ward, for-ward, to the Prom-ised Land.

136 SINCE JESUS CAME INTO MY HEART

R. H. McDaniel

Chas. H. Gabriel

1. What a won - der - ful change in my life has been wrought Since Je-sus came
2. I have ceased from my wand'ring and go - ing a - stray, Since Je-sus came
3. I'm pos-sessed of a hope that is stead-fast and sure, Since Je-sus came
4. There's a light in the val - ley of death now for me, Since Je-sus came
5. I shall go there to dwell in that cit - y I know, Since Je-sus came

in - to my heart; I have light in my soul for which long I had sought,
in - to my heart; And my sins which were man-y are all washed a - way,
in - to my heart; And no dark clouds of doubt now my path-way ob - scure,
in - to my heart; And the gates of the cit - y be - yond I can see,
in - to my heart; And I'm hap - py, so hap - py, as on - ward I go,

CHORUS

Since Je-sus came in - to my heart. Since Je-sus came in - to my
Since Je-sus came in, came

heart, Since Je-sus came in-to my heart; Floods of joy o'er my
in - to my heart, Since Je-sus came in, came in - to my heart;

soul like the sea - bil-lows roll, Since Je-sus came in - to my heart.

TRUST AND OBEY

Rev. J. H. Sammis

D. B. Towner

1. When we walk with the Lord In the light of His Word What a glo-ry He
2. Not a shad-ow can rise, Not a cloud in the skies, But His smile quickly
3. Not a bur-den we bear, Not a sor-row we share, But our toil He doth
4. But we nev-er can prove The de-lights of His love Un-til all on the
5. Then in fel-low-ship sweet We will sit at His feet, Or we'll walk by His

sheds on our way! While we do His good will, He a-bides with us still,
drives it a-way; Not a doubt or a fear, Not a sigh nor a tear,
rich-ly re-pay; Not a grief nor a loss, Not a frown nor a cross,
al-tar we lay; For the fa-vor He shows, And the joy He be-stows,
side in the way; What He says we will do, Where He sends we will go—

CHORUS

And with all who will trust and o-bey.
Can a-bide while we trust and o-bey.
But is blest if we trust and o-bey. Trust and o-bey, For there's
Are for them who will trust and o-bey.
Nev-er fear, on-ly trust and o-bey.

no oth-er way To be hap-py in Je-sus, But to trust and o-bey.

138 HE LEADETH ME

Joseph H. Gilmore

William B. Bradbury

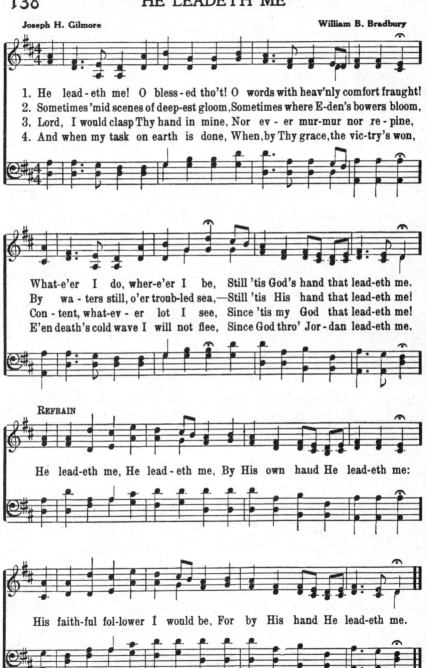

1. He lead-eth me! O bless-ed tho't! O words with heav'nly comfort fraught!
2. Sometimes 'mid scenes of deep-est gloom, Sometimes where E-den's bowers bloom,
3. Lord, I would clasp Thy hand in mine, Nor ev - er mur-mur nor re - pine,
4. And when my task on earth is done, When, by Thy grace, the vic-try's won,

What-e'er I do, wher-e'er I be, Still 'tis God's hand that lead-eth me.
By wa - ters still, o'er troub-led sea,—Still 'tis His hand that lead-eth me!
Con - tent, what-ev - er lot I see, Since 'tis my God that lead-eth me!
E'en death's cold wave I will not flee, Since God thro' Jor - dan lead-eth me.

REFRAIN

He lead-eth me, He lead - eth me, By His own hand He lead-eth me:

His faith-ful fol-lower I would be, For by His hand He lead-eth me.

139 BRINGING IN THE SHEAVES

KNOWLES SHAW

GEORGE A. MINOR

1. Sow-ing in the morn-ing, sow-ing seeds of kind-ness, Sow-ing in the
2. Sow-ing in the sun-shine, sow-ing in the shad-ows, Fear-ing nei-ther
3. Go-ing forth with weep-ing, sow-ing for the Mas-ter, Tho' the loss sus-

noon-tide and the dew-y eve; Wait-ing for the har-vest,
clouds nor win-ter's chill-ing breeze; By and by the har-vest,
tained our spir-it oft-en grieves; When our weep-ing's o-ver,

and the time of reap-ing, We shall come re-joic-ing, bring-ing in the sheaves.
and the la-bor end-ed, We shall come re-joic-ing, bring-ing in the sheaves.
He will bid us wel-come, We shall come re-joic-ing, bring-ing in the sheaves.

CHORUS

Bring-ing in the sheaves, bring-ing in the sheaves, We shall come re-joic-
Bring-ing in the sheaves, bring-ing in the sheaves, We shall come re-joic-

1 ing, bring-ing in the sheaves; 2 ing, bring-ing in the sheaves.

140 TELL OTHERS OF JESUS

Rev. Alfred Barratt

B. D. Ackley

1. There is a sto-ry more pre-cious than gold, Won-der-ful mes-sage that
2. Has-ten a-way while in sor-row they cry, 'Tis for the Gos-pel they
3. Car-ry the mes-sage to those in de-spair; Mil-lions in dark-ness are

can-not grow old; O-ver the world must this mes-sage be told—
hun-ger and sigh; Some one must tell them the news ere they die—
need-ing our care, While they are long-ing His bless-ings to share—

CHORUS.

Go and tell oth-ers of Je-sus. Go and tell oth-ers of

Je-sus, Go and tell oth-ers of Je-sus; Man-y in dark-ness are

wait-ing for you, Go and tell oth-ers of Je-sus.

TELL ME THE STORY OF JESUS

Fanny J. Crosby

Jno. R. Sweney

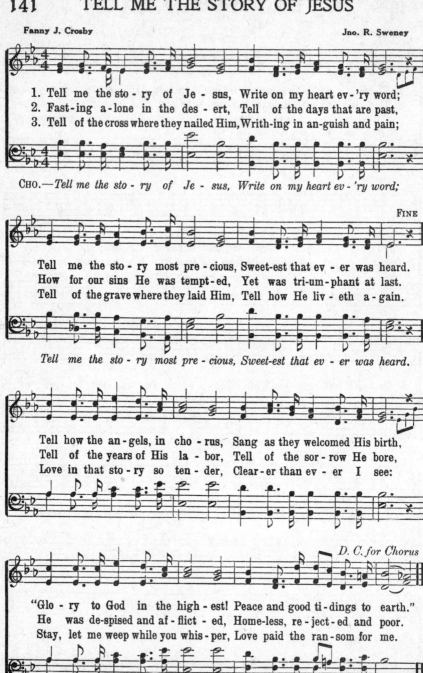

1. Tell me the sto - ry of Je - sus, Write on my heart ev - 'ry word;
2. Fast-ing a-lone in the des - ert, Tell of the days that are past,
3. Tell of the cross where they nailed Him, Writh-ing in an-guish and pain;

CHO.—*Tell me the sto - ry of Je - sus, Write on my heart ev -'ry word;*

FINE

Tell me the sto - ry most pre - cious, Sweet-est that ev - er was heard.
How for our sins He was tempt-ed, Yet was tri-um-phant at last.
Tell of the grave where they laid Him, Tell how He liv - eth a - gain.

Tell me the sto - ry most pre - cious, Sweet-est that ev - er was heard.

Tell how the an-gels, in cho - rus, Sang as they welcomed His birth,
Tell of the years of His la - bor, Tell of the sor - row He bore,
Love in that sto - ry so ten - der, Clear-er than ev - er I see:

D. C. for Chorus

"Glo - ry to God in the high-est! Peace and good ti-dings to earth."
He was de-spised and af - flict - ed, Home-less, re - ject-ed and poor.
Stay, let me weep while you whis - per, Love paid the ran-som for me.

142   TAKE UP THY CROSS

A. H. A.   Rev. A. H. Ackley.

Slowly, with expression.

1. I walked one day a-long a coun-try road, And there a stranger journeyed, too,
2. I cried, "Lord Jesus," and He spoke my name; I saw His hands all bruised and torn;
3. "O let me bear Thy cross, dear Lord," I cried, And, lo, a cross for me appeared,
4. My cross I'll car-ry till the crown appears, The way I jour-ney soon will end

Bent low beneath the bur-den of His load: It was a cross, a cross I knew.
I stooped to kiss away the marks of shame, The shame for me that He had borne.
The one for-got-ten I had cast a-side, The one, so long, that I had feared.
Where God Himself shall wipe a-way all tears, And friend hold fellowship with friend.

CHORUS

"Take up thy cross and fol-low Me." I hear the bless-ed Sav-ior call;

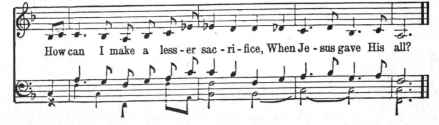

How can I make a less-er sac-ri-fice, When Je-sus gave His all?

143 WHAT WILL YOU DO?

F. G. Burroughs

Adam Geibel

1. What will you do with the King called Je-sus? Man-y are wait-ing to hear you say,—Some have despised Him, re-ject-ing His mer-cy, What will you do with your King to-day? What can you wit-ness con-cern-ing His good-ness, Who died to save you from sin's bit-ter thrall? Who will de-clare Him the fair-est of thou-sands? Who now will crown Him the Lord of all?

2. What will you do for the King called Je-sus,—He who for you left His throne a-bove, Here 'mid the low-ly and sin-ful to la-bor, Dai-ly un-fold-ing His Father's love? Look on the fields white al-read-y to har-vest, Who now is will-ing to toil with the few? What will you do for the dear Sav-ior, Je-sus? Lo, He is wait-ing, He calls for you!

3. What will you do with the King called Je-sus,—Who will sub-mit to His gen-tle sway? Where are the hearts read-y now to enthrone Him? Who will His kind com-mands o-bey? Come with your ointments most costly and pre-cious, Pour out your gifts at the dear Sav-ior's feet; Ren-der to Him all your loy-al de-vo-tion; Seek to ex-alt Him by prais-es meet.

WHAT WILL YOU DO?

CHORUS *Unison*

What will you do with the King called Je-sus? What, oh, what will you do with Je-sus?

Parts

He waits to bless all who humbly con-fess Faith in His blood and right-eous-ness.

144 AWAKE, MY SOUL, IN JOYFUL LAYS

Rev. Samuel Medley   Western Melody

1. A - wake, my soul, in joy-ful lays, And sing thy great Re-deem-er's praise;
2. He saw me ru - ined in the fall, Yet loved me not - with-stand-ing all,
3. Thro' might-y hosts of cru - el foes, Where earth and hell my way op - pose,
4. Oft - en I feel my sin - ful heart, Prone from my Je - sus to de-part;

He just-ly claims a song from me, His lov-ing-kind-ness is so free.
And saved me from my lost es - tate, His lov-ing-kind - ness is so great.
He safe-ly leads my soul a - long, His lov-ing-kind - ness is so strong.
And tho' I oft have Him for-got, His lov-ing-kind - ness changes not.

Lov - ing-kind-ness, lov - ing-kind-ness, His lov - ing-kind - ness is so free.
Lov - ing-kind-ness, lov - ing-kind-ness, His lov - ing-kind - ness is so great.
Lov - ing-kind-ness, lov - ing-kind-ness, His lov - ing-kind - ness is so strong.
Lov - ing-kind-ness, lov - ing-kind-ness, His lov - ing-kind - ness changes not.

145 "GREAT IS THY FAITHFULNESS"

T. O. Chisholm

William. M. Runyan

1. "Great is Thy faith-ful-ness," O God my Fa-ther, There is no shad-ow of
2. Sum-mer and winter, and spring-time and harvest, Sun, moon and stars in their
3. Par-don for sin and a peace that en-dur-eth, Thine own dear presence to

turning with Thee; Thou changest not, Thy compassions, they fail not, As Thou hast
cours-es a-bove, Join with all na-ture in man-i-fold wit-ness, To Thy great
cheer and to guide; Strength for to-day and bright hope for to-morrow, Blessings all

CHORUS

been Thou for-ev-er wilt be."
faith-ful-ness, mer-cy and love. "Great is Thy faith-ful-ness! Great is Thy
mine, with ten thou-sand be-side!

faith-ful-ness!" Morn-ing by morn-ing new mer-cies I see; All I have

rall.

need-ed Thy hand hath provided,—"Great is Thy faithfulness," Lord, un-to me!

"WHOSOEVER WILL"

146

P. P. B.

P. P. Bliss

1. "Who-so-ev-er hear - eth," shout, shout the sound! Spread the bless-ed ti-dings
2. Who-so-ev-er com - eth, need not de-lay, Now the door is o - pen,
3. "Who-so-ev-er will!" the prom-ise is se-cure; "Who-so-ev-er will," for-

all the world a-round; Tell the joy-ful news wher-ev-er man is found,
en-ter while you may; Je - sus is the true, the on-ly Liv-ing Way:
ev-er must en-dure; "Who-so-ev-er will!" 'tis life for-ev-er-more;

CHORUS

"Who-so-ev-er will may come." "Who-so-ev-er will, who-so-ev-er will!"

Send the proc-la-ma-tion o-ver vale and hill; 'Tis a lov-ing

Fa-ther calls the wan-d'rer home: "Who-so-ev-er will may come."

147   IS IT THE CROWNING DAY?

George Walker Whitcomb   Charles H. Marsh

1. Je - sus may come to - day, Glad day, Glad day! And I would see my
2. I may go home to - day, Glad day, Glad day! Seemeth I hear their
3. Why should I anxious be? Glad day, Glad day! Lights appear on the
4. Faith-ful I'll be to - day, Glad day, Glad day! And I will free - ly

Friend; Dangers and troubles would end If Je - sus should come to -
song; Hail to the ra - di - ant throng! If I should go home to -
shore, Storms will affright nev-er - more, For He is "at hand" to -
tell Why I should love Him so well, For He is my all to -

REFRAIN.

day. Glad day, Glad day! Is it the crown - ing day? I'll

live for to - day, nor anx - ious be; Je - sus, my Lord I

rit.

soon shall see. Glad day, Glad day! Is it the crown-ing day?

148 THERE'S A GREAT DAY COMING

W. L. Thompson

W. L. Thompson

1. There's a great day com-ing, A great day com-ing, There's a great day com-ing by and by, When the saints and the sin-ners shall be part - ed right and left, Are you read-y for that day to come?

2. There's a bright day com-ing, A bright day com-ing, There's a bright day com-ing by and by, But its bright-ness shall on - ly come to them that love the Lord, Are you read-y for that day to come?

3. There's a sad day com-ing, A sad day com-ing, There's a sad day com-ing by and by, When the sin - ner shall hear his doom, "De- part, I know ye not!" Are you read-y for that day to come?

CHORUS

Are you read-y? Are you read-y? Are you ready for the judgment day? Are you read-y? Are you read-y for the judgment day?

149 WHAT IF IT WERE TODAY?

Mrs. C. H. M.   Mrs. C. H. Morris.

1. Je - sus is com-ing to earth a-gain, What if it were to - day?
2. Sa - tan's do-min-ion will then be o'er, O that it were to - day!
3. Faithful and true would He find us here If He should come to - day?

Com - ing in pow - er and love to reign, What if it were to - day?
Sor - row and sigh-ing shall be no more, O that it were to - day!
Watching in gladness and not in fear, If He should come to - day?

Com-ing to claim His cho - sen Bride, All the redeem'd and pur - i - fied,
Then shall the dead in Christ a-rise, Caught up to meet Him in the skies,
Signs of His com-ing mul - ti-ply, Morning light breaks in east-ern sky,

rit. *a tempo*

O - ver this whole earth scattered wide, What if it were to - day?
When shall these glories meet our eyes? What if it were to - day?
Watch, for the time is draw-ing nigh, What if it were to - day?

CHORUS.

Glo - ry! glo - ry! joy to my heart 'twill bring;
joy to my heart 'twill bring,

WHAT IF IT WERE TODAY?

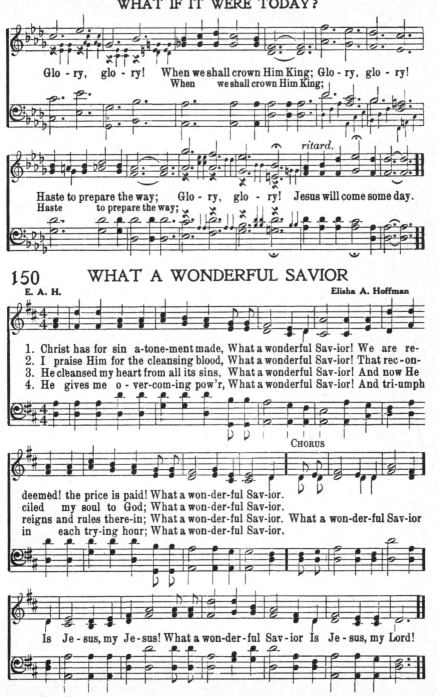

Glo - ry, glo - ry! When we shall crown Him King; Glo - ry, glo - ry!
When we shall crown Him King;

ritard.

Haste to prepare the way; Glo - ry, glo - ry! Jesus will come some day.
Haste to prepare the way;

150 WHAT A WONDERFUL SAVIOR

E. A. H.

Elisha A. Hoffman

1. Christ has for sin a-tone-ment made, What a wonderful Sav-ior! We are re-
2. I praise Him for the cleansing blood, What a wonderful Sav-ior! That rec-on-
3. He cleansed my heart from all its sins, What a wonderful Sav-ior! And now He
4. He gives me o - ver-com-ing pow'r, What a wonderful Sav-ior! And tri-umph

CHORUS

deemed! the price is paid! What a won-der-ful Sav-ior.
ciled my soul to God; What a won-der-ful Sav-ior.
reigns and rules there-in; What a won-der-ful Sav-ior. What a won-der-ful Sav-ior
in each try-ing hour; What a won-der-ful Sav-ior.

Is Je - sus, my Je - sus! What a won-der-ful Sav - ior Is Je - sus, my Lord!

151   WILL JESUS FIND US WATCHING?

Fanny J. Crosby

W. H. Doane

1. When Je - sus comes to re - ward His serv-ants, Wheth-er it be
2. If at the dawn of the ear - ly morn-ing, He shall call us
3. Have we been true to the trust He left us? Do we seek to
4. Bless - ed are those whom the Lord finds watching, In His glo - ry

noon or night, Faith - ful to Him, will He find us watch-ing,
one by one, When to the Lord we re - store our tal - ents,
do our best? If in our hearts there is naught con-demns us,
they shall share; If He shall come at the dawn or mid-night,

rit.

CHORUS

With our lamps all trimmed and bright?
Will He an - swer Thee—Well done?   O can we say we are
We shall have a glo - rious rest.
Will He find us watch - ing there?

read - y, broth-er, Read - y for the soul's bright home? Say, will He

find you and me still watching, Wait-ing, waiting, when the Lord shall come?

CHRIST RETURNETH

H. L. Turner

James McGranahan

1. It may be at morn, when the day is a - wak-ing, When sunlight thro'
2. It may be at mid - day, it may be at twi-light, It may be, per-
3. While its hosts cry Hosanna, from heaven de-scend-ing, With glo - ri - fied
4. Oh, joy! oh, de-light! should we go with-out dy - ing, No sick-ness, no

dark - ness and shad-ow is break-ing, That Je - sus will come in the
chance, that the black-ness of mid-night Will burst in - to light in the
saints and the an - gels at-tend-ing, With grace on His brow, like a
sad - ness, no dread and no cry - ing, Caught up thro' the clouds with our

full - ness of glo - ry, To re - ceive from the world "His own."
blaze of His glo - ry, When Je - sus re - ceives "His own."
ha - lo of glo - ry, Will Je - sus re - ceive "His own."
Lord in - to glo - ry, When Je - sus re - ceives "His own."

CHORUS

O Lord Je - sus, how long, how long Ere we shout the glad song, Christ re-

rit.

turn-eth! Hal-le - lu-jah! hal-le - lu-jah! A - men, Hal-le - lu-jah! A - men.

153 JESUS SET THE MUSIC RINGING

Rev. George O. Webster

C. Austin Miles

1. You ask what makes me hap-py The whole day long, Why I am al-ways
2. I can-not keep from sing-ing Since that glad day, When Je-sus took, in
3. His love each day is grow-ing More sweet to me, Each day new grace and

sing-ing A glad-some song; Ah, well do I re-mem-ber When
mer-cy, My sins a-way; He o-pened up a foun-tain Whence
beau-ty In Him I see; For all this world can of-fer From

song be-gan to start, 'Twas Je-sus set the mu-sic Ring-ing in my heart.
streams of gladness start, 'Twas Je-sus set the mu-sic Ring-ing in my heart.
Him I would not part, Since He has set the mu-sic Ring-ing in my heart.

CHORUS

In my heart . . . He set the mu-sic ringing, In my life . . . . a heav'n-ly

In my heart

In my life

glad-ness bringing; Ah, well do I re-mem-ber When song be-gan to start,

JESUS SET THE MUSIC RINGING

rit.

'Twas Je - sus set the mu - sic Ring-ing in my heart.
Ring-ing, ring - ing in my heart.

154 HEAVENLY SUNLIGHT

Rev. H. J. Zelley

G. H. Cook

1. Walk-ing in sun-light, all of my jour - ney, O - ver the moun-tains,
2. Shad-ows a - round me, shad-ows a - bove me, Nev - er con - ceal my
3. In the bright sun - light, ev - er re - joic - ing, Press-ing my way to

thru the deep vale; Je - sus has said, "I'll nev - er for-sake thee," Prom-ise di -
Sav - ior and Guide; He is the light, in Him is no dark-ness, Ev - er I'm
man-sions a - bove; Singing His prais-es, glad-ly I'm walk-ing, Walk-ing in

D. S.—*Sing-ing His*

FINE. CHORUS

vine that nev - er shall fail.
'walk-ing close to His side. Heav-en-ly sun-light, heav-en-ly sun-light,
sun - light, sun-light of love.

prais - es, Je - sus is mine.

D. S.

Flood-ing my soul with glo - ry di - vine; Hal - le - lu - jah! I am re-joic-ing,

155 JESUS, I MY CROSS HAVE TAKEN

HENRY F. LYTE

From MOZART

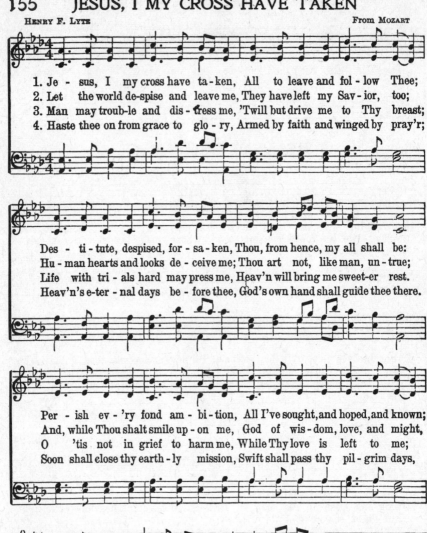

1. Je - sus, I my cross have ta - ken, All to leave and fol - low Thee;
2. Let the world de-spise and leave me, They have left my Sav - ior, too;
3. Man may troub-le and dis - tress me, 'Twill but drive me to Thy breast;
4. Haste thee on from grace to glo - ry, Armed by faith and winged by pray'r;

Des - ti - tute, despised, for - sa - ken, Thou, from hence, my all shall be:
Hu - man hearts and looks de - ceive me; Thou art not, like man, un - true;
Life with tri - als hard may press me, Heav'n will bring me sweet-er rest.
Heav'n's e-ter - nal days be - fore thee, God's own hand shall guide thee there.

Per - ish ev - 'ry fond am - bi - tion, All I've sought, and hoped, and known;
And, while Thou shalt smile up - on me, God of wis - dom, love, and might;
O 'tis not in grief to harm me, While Thy love is left to me;
Soon shall close thy earth - ly mission, Swift shall pass thy pil - grim days,

Yet how rich is my con - di-tion, God and heav'n are still my own!
Foes may hate and friends may shun me; Show Thy face, and all is bright.
O 'twere not in joy to charm me, Were that joy unmixed with Thee.
Hope shall change to glad fru-i - tion, Faith to sight, and pray'r to praise. A-men.

156 BENEATH THE CROSS OF JESUS

Elizabeth C. Clephane   Frederick C. Maker

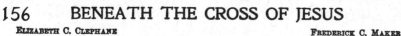

1. Be-neath the cross of Je - sus I fain would take my stand,
2. Up - on that cross of Je - sus Mine eye at times can see
3. I take, O cross, thy shad - ow For my a - bid - ing place;

The shad - ow of a might - y rock With - in a wea - ry land;
The ver - y dy - ing form of One Who suf - fered there for me;
I ask no oth - er sun-shine than The sun - shine of His face;

A home with - in the wil - der - ness, A rest up - on the way,
And from my smit - ten heart with tears Two won - ders I con - fess,—
Con - tent to let the world go by, To know no gain or loss,

From the burning of the noon-tide heat, And the bur-den of the day.
The won - ders of His glo-rious love And my un-wor - thi - ness.
My sin - ful self my on - ly shame, My glo - ry all the cross.

157 WHEN I SURVEY THE WONDROUS CROSS

ISAAC WATTS   HAMBURG. L. M.   Arr. by LOWELL MASON

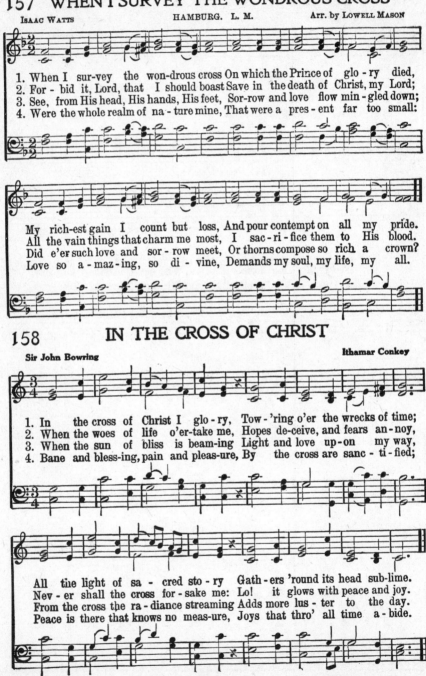

1. When I sur-vey the won-drous cross On which the Prince of glo-ry died,
2. For - bid it, Lord, that I should boast Save in the death of Christ, my Lord;
3. See, from His head, His hands, His feet, Sor-row and love flow min-gled down;
4. Were the whole realm of na-ture mine, That were a pres-ent far too small:

My rich-est gain I count but loss, And pour contempt on all my pride.
All the vain things that charm me most, I sac-ri-fice them to His blood.
Did e'er such love and sor - row meet, Or thorns compose so rich a crown?
Love so a - maz-ing, so di - vine, Demands my soul, my life, my all.

158   IN THE CROSS OF CHRIST

Sir John Bowring   Ithamar Conkey

1. In the cross of Christ I glo-ry, Tow-'ring o'er the wrecks of time;
2. When the woes of life o'er-take me, Hopes de-ceive, and fears an-noy,
3. When the sun of bliss is beam-ing Light and love up-on my way,
4. Bane and bless-ing, pain and pleas-ure, By the cross are sanc-ti-fied;

All the light of sa - cred sto-ry Gath-ers 'round its head sub-lime.
Nev-er shall the cross for-sake me: Lo! it glows with peace and joy.
From the cross the ra-diance streaming Adds more lus-ter to the day.
Peace is there that knows no meas-ure, Joys that thro' all time a-bide.

159 THE CHRIST OF THE CROSS

F. C. H.

Frank C. Huston

Slowly, tenderly

1. On Cal - va-ry's brow there was plant-ed a cross, Which lift - ed a
2. They knew not their deeds of that one might-y hour, "O Fa - ther, for-
3. Let oth - ers, who will, praise the cross of the Christ, The Christ of the

Inst.

man up to shame; But He on the cross was the dear Son of God,
give them," He cried; They knew not the cross, long the em - blem of shame,
cross, is my theme; For tho' we must cher-ish the old rug-ged cross,

CHORUS f

Who died a lost world to re - claim.
Was there by the Christ glo-ri - fied.
'Tis on - ly the Christ can re-deem.
The Christ of the cross is the

ff   f

theme of my song, The won-der-ful Christ of the cross. He a-tone-ment has

ff   dim. rall.

made; He my ran-som has paid, So I'll praise Him, { The / My } Christ of the cross.

160   YE SERVANTS OF GOD

C. Wesley   F. J. Haydn

1. Ye serv-ants of God, your Mas-ter pro-claim, And pub-lish a-
2. God rul-eth on high, al-might-y to save; And still He is
3. Sal-va-tion to God, who sits on the throne, Let all cry a-
4. Then let us a-dore and give Him His right, All glo-ry, and

broad His won-der-ful name; The name all-vic-to-rious of
nigh—His pres-ence we have; The great con-gre-ga-tion His
loud and hon-or the Son; The prais-es of Je-sus the
pow'r, and wis-dom and might; All hon-or and bless-ing, with

Je-sus ex-tol; His king-dom is glo-rious, He rules o-ver all.
tri-umph shall sing, As-crib-ing sal-va-tion to Je-sus our King.
an-gels pro-claim, Fall down on their fac-es and wor-ship the Lamb.
an-gels a-bove, And thanks nev-er ceas-ing, and in-fi-nite love.

161   MUST JESUS BEAR THE CROSS ALONE?

Thos. Shepherd   Geo. N. Allen

1. Must Je-sus bear the cross a-lone, And all the world go free?
2. How hap-py are the saints a-bove, Who once went sor-rowing here!
3. The con-se-cra-ted cross I'll bear, Till death shall set me free;
4. Up-on the crys-tal pave-ment, down At Je-sus' pierc-ed feet,

MUST JESUS BEAR THE CROSS ALONE?

No, there's a cross for ev - 'ry one, And there's a cross for me.
But now they taste un - min - gled love, And joy with-out a tear.
And then go home my crown to wear, For there's a crown for me.
Joy - ful, I'll cast my gold - en crown, And His dear name re - peat.

162

NEAR THE CROSS

Fanny J. Crosby

W. H. Doane

1. Je - sus, keep me near the cross, There a pre - cious foun - tain
2. Near the cross, a trem-bling soul, Love and mer - cy found me;
3. Near the cross! O Lamb of God, Bring its scenes be - fore me;
4. Near the cross I'll watch and wait, Hop-ing, trust-ing ev - er,

Free to all— a heal - ing stream, Flows from Cal-v'ry's moun - tain.
There the Bright and Morn - ing Star Sheds its beams a - round me.
Help me walk from day to day, With its shad-ows o'er me.
Till I reach the gold - en strand, Just be - yond the riv - er.

CHORUS

In the cross, in the cross, Be my glo - ry ev - er;

Till my rap-tured soul shall find Rest be - yond the riv - er.

163 LEAD ME, SAVIOUR

"For thy name's sake, lead me and guide me."—Ps. 31 : 3

F. M. D.

FRANK M. DAVIS. By per.

With expression

1. Sav - iour, lead me, lest I stray,
2. Thou the ref - uge of my soul,
3. Sav - iour, lead me till at last,

1. Sav - iour, lead me, lest I stray, Gen - tly

Gen - tly lead me all the
When life's storm - y bil - lows
When the storm of life is

way;
roll;
past,

I am safe when by Thy side,
I am safe when Thou art nigh,
I shall reach the land of day,

lead me all the way; I am safe when by Thy side,

Chorus

I would in Thy love a - bide (love a-bide).
All my hopes on Thee re - ly (I re - ly).
Where all tears are wiped a - way (wiped a-way).

I would in Thy love a - bide.

Lead me, lead me,

Sav - iour, lead me, lest I stray;........... Gen - tly

lest I stray;

down the stream of time, Lead me, Sav - iour, all the way.

Changing stream of time,

all the way.

164 THE WAY OF THE CROSS LEADS HOME

JESSIE BROWN POUNDS   CHAS. H. GABRIEL

1. I must needs go home by the way of the cross, There's no oth-er
2. I must needs go on in the blood-sprinkled way, The path that the
3. Then I bid fare-well to the way of the world, To walk in it

way but this; I shall ne'er get sight of the Gates of Light,
Sav-ior trod, If I ev-er climb to the heights sub-lime,
nev-er-more; For my Lord says "Come," and I seek my home,

If the way of the cross I miss.
Where the soul is at home with God.
Where He waits at the o-pen door.

CHORUS.

The way of the cross leads home, The way of the cross leads home; It is
leads home,   leads home;

sweet to know, as I on-ward go, The way of the cross leads home. A-MEN.

SOMEBODY CARES

Fannie Edna Stafford

Homer A. Rodeheaver

1. Some-bod-y knows when your heart aches, And ev'ry-thing seems to go wrong;
2. Some-bod-y cares when you're tempted, And your mind grows diz-zy and dim;
3. Some-bod-y loves you when wea - ry; ⟩ Some-bod-y loves you when strong;

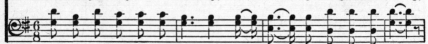

Some-bod-y knows when the shad-ows Need chas-ing a - way with a song;
Some-bod-y cares when you're weakest, And far-thest a - way from Him;
Al - ways is wait-ing to help you, He watch-es you—one of the throng

Some-bod - y knows when you're lone - ly, Tir - ed, dis-cour-aged and blue;
Some-bod - y grieves when you're fall - en, You are not lost from His sight;
Need-ing His friend-ship so ho - ly, Needing His watch-care so true;

Some-bod-y wants you to know Him, And know that He dear - ly loves you.
Some-bod-y waits for your com - ing, And He'll drive the gloom from your night.
His name? We call His name Je - sus; He loves ev - 'ry one, He loves you.

166 IT IS WELL WITH MY SOUL

H. G. Spafford

P. P. Bliss

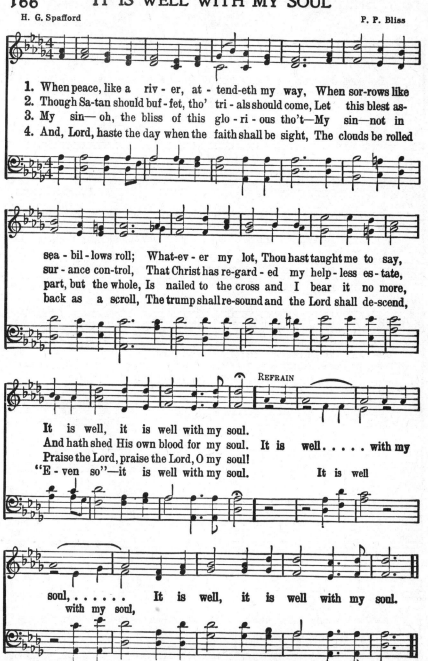

1. When peace, like a riv - er, at - tend-eth my way, When sor-rows like
2. Though Sa-tan should buf - fet, tho' tri - als should come, Let this blest as-
3. My sin— oh, the bliss of this glo - ri - ous tho't—My sin—not in
4. And, Lord, haste the day when the faith shall be sight, The clouds be rolled

sea - bil - lows roll; What-ev - er my lot, Thou hast taught me to say,
sur - ance con-trol, That Christ has re-gard - ed my help - less es - tate,
part, but the whole, Is nailed to the cross and I bear it no more,
back as a scroll, The trump shall re-sound and the Lord shall de-scend,

REFRAIN

It is well, it is well with my soul.
And hath shed His own blood for my soul. It is well . . . . . with my
Praise the Lord, praise the Lord, O my soul!
"E - ven so"—it is well with my soul. It is well

soul, ... It is well, it is well with my soul.
with my soul,

167 BRIGHTEN THE CORNER WHERE YOU ARE

INA DULEY OGDON

CHAS. H. GABRIEL

1. Do not wait un-til some deed of great-ness you may do, Do not
2. Just a-bove are cloud-ed skies that you may help to clear, Let not
3. Here for all your tal-ent you may sure-ly find a need, Here re-

wait to shed your light a-far, To the man-y du-ties ev-er near you
nar-row self your way de-bar, Tho' in-to one heart a-lone may fall your
flect the Bright and Morning Star, E-ven from your humble hand the bread of

REFRAIN

now be true, Bright-en the cor-ner where you are.
song of cheer, Bright-en the cor-ner where you are. Bright-en the cor-ner
life may feed, Bright-en the cor-ner where you are.

where you are! Bright-en the cor-ner where you are! Some one far from
Shine for Je-sus where you are!

har-bor you may guide a-cross the bar, Bright-en the cor-ner where you are.

168 IN THE GARDEN

C. A. M.

C. Austin Miles

1. I come to the gar-den a - lone, While the dew is still on the
2. He speaks, and the sound of His voice Is so sweet the birds hush their
3. I'd stay in the gar-den with Him Tho' the night a-round me be

ros - es; And the voice I hear, Fall-ing on my ear; The
sing - ing, And the mel - o - dy That He gave to me, With-
fall - ing, But He bids me go; Thru the voice of woe, His

CHORUS

Son of God dis-clos - es.
in my heart is ring - ing. And He walks with me, and He
voice to me is call - ing.

talks with me, And He tells me I am His own, And the

joy we share as we tar - ry there, None oth-er has ev - er known.

169 HE KEEPS ON LOVING US STILL

Herbert Buffum

Haldor Lillenas

1. Though far you may wan-der a-way from the fold, Re-fus-ing to
2. His love is far great-er than mor-tals have known, His mer-cy the
3. Though fa-ther or moth-er for-sake us, we know This lov-er of
4. Should we for-sake Him and our love be-come cold, No lon-ger our

yield to His will, This thought is so pre-cious, al-though it be old:
whole earth doth fill; To those who de-ny Him what pa-tience is shown!
souls nev-er will; He fol-lows our foot-steps, wher-e'er they may go,
hearts feel the thrill That once we en-joyed when we en-tered His fold,

CHORUS

"He keeps on lov-ing us still."
He keeps on lov-ing us still. He keeps on lov-ing us
And keeps on lov-ing us still.
He will keep on lov-ing us still.

still, ... He keeps on lov-ing us still. . . . . Come
lov-ing us still, lov-ing us still.

loss or come gain, Thru sun-shine or rain, He keeps on lov-ing us still.

170 SPEAK, MY LORD

G. B.

COPYRIGHT 1911, RENEWAL 1939 BY GEO. BENNARD

George Bennard

1. Hear the Lord of har-vest sweet-ly call-ing, "Who will go and
2. When the coal of fire . . touched the proph-et, Mak-ing him as
3. Mil-lions now in sin and shame are dy-ing, Lis-ten to their
4. Soon the time for reap-ing will be o-ver; Soon we'll gath-er

work for Me to-day? Who will bring to Me the lost and dy-ing?
pure, as pure can be, When the voice of God said,"Who'll go for us?"
sad and bit-ter cry; Has-ten, broth-er, has-ten to the res-cue;
for the har-vest-home; May the Lord of har-vest smile up-on us,

CHORUS

Who will point them to the nar-row way?"
Then he an-swered,"Here I am, send me." Speak, my Lord, speak, my
Quick-ly an-swer,"Mas-ter, here am I."
May we hear His bless-ed,"Child, well done." Speak, my Lord,

Lord, Speak, and I'll be quick to an-swer Thee; Speak, my
Speak, my Lord, to answer Thee;

rit.

Lord, speak, my Lord, Speak, and I will answer,"Lord, send me."
Speak, my Lord, "Lord, send me."

171 HE KEEPS ME SINGING

L. B. B.   L. B. BRIDGERS

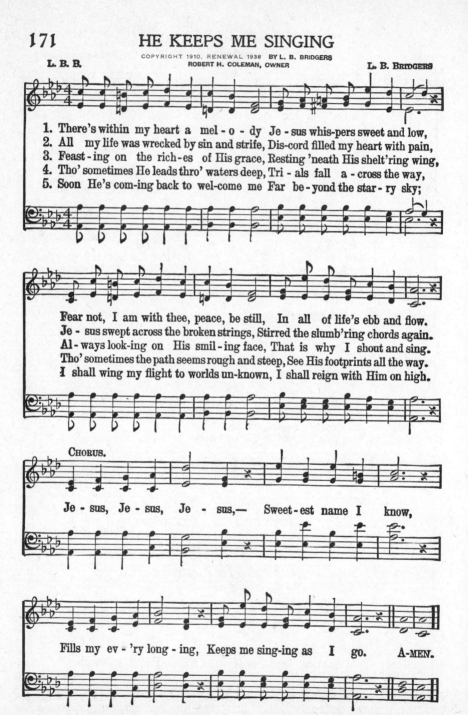

1. There's within my heart a mel-o-dy Je-sus whis-pers sweet and low,
2. All my life was wrecked by sin and strife, Dis-cord filled my heart with pain,
3. Feast-ing on the rich-es of His grace, Resting 'neath His shelt'ring wing,
4. Tho' sometimes He leads thro' waters deep, Tri-als fall a-cross the way,
5. Soon He's com-ing back to wel-come me Far be-yond the star-ry sky;

Fear not, I am with thee, peace, be still, In all of life's ebb and flow.
Je-sus swept across the broken strings, Stirred the slumb'ring chords again.
Al-ways look-ing on His smil-ing face, That is why I shout and sing.
Tho' sometimes the path seems rough and steep, See His footprints all the way.
I shall wing my flight to worlds un-known, I shall reign with Him on high.

CHORUS.

Je-sus, Je-sus, Je-sus,— Sweet-est name I know,

Fills my ev-'ry long-ing, Keeps me sing-ing as I go.   A-MEN.

172 HE'S A WONDERFUL SAVIOR TO ME

Virgil P. Brock   Blanche Kerr Brock

1. I was lost in sin, but Je-sus res-cued me, He's a won-der-ful
2. He's a Friend so true, so pa-tient and so kind, He's a won-der-ful
3. He is al-ways near to com-fort and to cheer, He's a won-der-ful
4. Dear-er grows the love of Je-sus day by day, He's a won-der-ful

Sav-ior to me; I was bound by fear, but Je-sus set me free,
Sav-ior to me; Ev-'ry-thing I need in Him I al-ways find,
Sav-ior to me;(So wonderful!) He for-gives my sins, He dries my ev-'ry tear,
Sav-ior to me; Sweet-er is His grace while pressing on my way,

CHORUS.

He's a won-der-ful Sav-ior to me.(So won-der-full) For He's a won-der-ful

Sav-ior to me,   He's a won-der-ful Sav-ior to me;
              won-der-full   won-der-full

I was lost in sin, but Je-sus took me in: He's a wonderful Sav-ior to me.

173 WHEN THE ROLL IS CALLED UP YONDER

J. M. B.

J. M. Black

1. When the trumpet of the Lord shall sound, and time shall be no more, And the
2. On that bright and cloudless morning when the dead in Christ shall rise, And the
3. Let us la - bor for the Mas - ter from the dawn till set - ting sun, Let us

morning breaks, e-ter-nal, bright and fair; When the saved of earth shall gather
glo - ry of His res - ur-rec-tion share; When His cho-sen ones shall gather
talk of all His wondrous love and care; Then when all of life is o - ver,

o - ver on the oth-er shore, And the roll is called up yon-der, I'll be there.
to their home beyond the skies, And the roll is called up yon-der, I'll be there.
and our work on earth is done, And the roll is called up yon-der, I'll be there.

CHORUS.

When the roll . . . . . . is called up yon - - - - - der, When the
When the roll is called up yon - der, I'll be there,

roll . . . . is called up yon - - der, When the roll . . . . is called up
When the roll is called up yon-der, I'll be there, When the roll is called up

WHEN THE ROLL IS CALLED UP YONDER

yon - der, When the roll is called up yon - der, I'll be there.

174   THE CLEANSING WAVE

Mrs. Phœbe Palmer   Mrs. Joseph F. Knapp

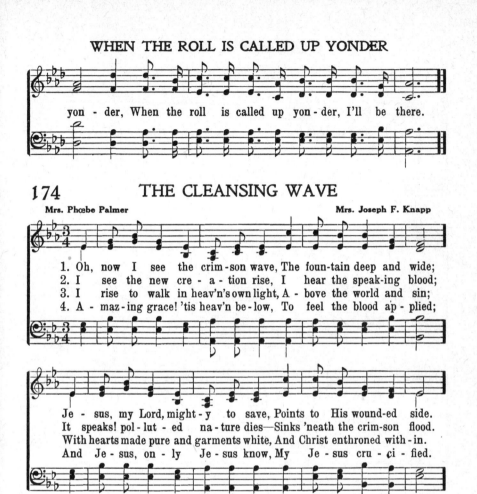

1. Oh, now I see the crim-son wave, The foun-tain deep and wide;
2. I see the new cre - a - tion rise, I hear the speak-ing blood;
3. I rise to walk in heav'n's own light, A - bove the world and sin;
4. A - maz-ing grace! 'tis heav'n be - low, To feel the blood ap - plied;

Je - sus, my Lord, might - y to save, Points to His wound-ed side.
It speaks! pol - lut - ed na - ture dies—Sinks 'neath the crim-son flood.
With hearts made pure and garments white, And Christ enthroned with - in.
And Je - sus, on - ly Je - sus know, My Je - sus cru - ci - fied.

CHORUS

The cleans-ing stream I see, I see! I plunge, and oh, it cleans-eth me;

Oh, praise the Lord, it cleans-eth me, It cleans-eth me, yes, cleans-eth me.

175   WONDERFUL MERCY

E. E. Hewitt.

B. D. Ackley.

1. Won-der-ful fountain that cleans-eth from sin, Won-der-ful com-fort, a-
2. Won-der-ful prom-is - es, meet-ing my need, Won-der-ful answers, my
3. Won-der-ful mansion that shin-eth so far, Lit by my Sav-ior, e-

bid - ing with - in, Peace rolling in like the waves of the sea; Won-der-ful
pray'rs far ex - ceed; Won-der-ful help for the work of each hour; Strength for the
ter - ni - ty's Star: There I shall praise Him with Eden's bright throng Wonderful

CHORUS.

freedom, when Christ makes us free.
con - flict, vic - tor - i - ous pow'r. Wonderful, won-der-ful mer-cy I sing,
coun - try, O won-der-ful song!

Wonderful grace of my won-der-ful King: Won-der-ful fav - or from

heav - en a - bove, Won-der-ful mer - cy, won - der - ful love.

176 ALL THE WAY MY SAVIOR LEADS

Fanny J. Crosby

Robert Lowry

1. All the way my Sav-ior leads me; What have I to ask be-side?
2. All the way my Sav-ior leads me; Cheers each winding path I tread;
3. All the way my Sav-ior leads me; O the full-ness of His love!

Can I doubt His ten-der mer-cy Who thru life has been my guide?
Gives me grace for ev-'ry tri-al, Feeds me with the liv-ing bread;
Per-fect rest to me is prom-ised In my Fa-ther's house a-bove;

Heav'n-ly peace, di-vin-est com-fort, Here by faith in Him to dwell!
Tho' my wea-ry steps may fal-ter, And my soul a-thirst may be,
When my spir-it, clothed im-mor-tal, Wings its flight to realms of day,

For I know, what-e'er be-fall me, Je-sus do-eth all things well;
Gush-ing from the Rock be-fore me, Lo! a spring of joy I see;
This my song thru end-less a-ges—Je-sus led me all the way;

For I know, what-e'er be-fall me, Je-sus do-eth all things well.
Gush-ing from the Rock be-fore me, Lo! a spring of joy I see.
This my song thru end-less a-ges—Je-sus led me all the way.

177 I HAVE BEEN SAVED

Ina Duley Ogdon

Chas. H. Gabriel

1. My glad heart is sing-ing by day and by night, My soul o-ver-
2. O would that my tongue with His truth were a-flame, For life would I
3. His mer-cy, His good-ness can nev-er be told, And heav-en a-

flows with a won-drous de-light, My joy would I share with a sin-wea-ry race,
give by the pow'r of His name; Some day I shall look on His beau-ti-ful face,
lone shall His glo-ries un-fold, And there He has gone to prepare me a place,

Chorus

For I have been saved by grace. Saved! hal-le-lu-jah!

I have been

Saved! hal-le-lu-jah! Saved by His won-der-ful, mar-vel-ous grace!

I have been

I'll sing of His love till I meet Him a-bove, For I have been saved by grace.

178 SWEET PEACE, THE GIFT OF GOD'S LOVE

P. P. B.

P. P. BILHORN

1. There comes to my heart one sweet strain, (sweet strain,) A glad and a
2. Thro' Christ on the cross peace was made, (was made,) My debt by His
3. When Je - sus as Lord I had crowned, (had crowned,) My heart with this
4. In Je - sus for peace I a - bide, (a - bide,) And as I keep

joy - ous re - frain; (re-frain;) I sing it a - gain and a - gain,
death was all paid; (all paid;) No oth - er foun - da - tion is laid,
peace did a-bound; (abound;) In Him the rich bless - ing I found,
close to His side; (His side,) There's nothing but peace doth be - tide,

CHORUS

Sweet peace, the gift of God's love.
For peace, the gift of God's love.
Sweet peace, the gift of God's love.
Sweet peace, the gift of God's love.

Peace, peace, sweet peace!

cres.

Won - der - ful gift from a - bove! (a - bove!) Oh, won - der - ful,

won - der - ful peace! Sweet peace, the gift of God's love!

179 LEANING ON THE EVERLASTING ARMS

Rev. E. A. Hoffman

A. J. Showalter

1. What a fel-low-ship, what a joy Di-vine, Lean-ing on the
2. O how sweet to walk in this pil-grim way, Lean-ing on the
3. What have I to dread, what have I to fear, Lean-ing on the

Ev - er - last - ing Arms! What a bless-ed-ness, what a peace is mine,
Ev - er - last - ing Arms! O how bright the path grows from day to day,
Ev - er - last - ing Arms! I have peace com-plete with my Lord so near,

REFRAIN

Lean - ing on the Ev - er - last - ing Arms! Lean - - ing,
Lean-ing on Je - sus,

lean - ing, Safe and se-cure from all a-larms; Lean - ing,
Lean-ing on Je - sus, Lean-ing on Je - sus,

lean - - ing, Lean - ing on the Ev - er - last - ing Arms.
Lean - ing on Je - sus,

180 LOVE LIFTED ME

James Rowe   Howard E. Smith

1. I was sink-ing deep in sin, Far from the peaceful shore, Ver-y deep-ly
2. All my heart to Him I give, Ev-er to Him I'll cling, In His bless-ed
3. Souls in dan-ger, look a-bove, Je-sus com-plete-ly saves; He will lift you

stained with-in, Sink-ing to rise no more; But the Mas-ter of the sea
pres-ence live, Ev-er His prais-es' sing. Love so might-y and so true
by His love Out of the an-gry waves. He's the Mas-ter of the sea,

Heard my de-spair-ing cry, From the wa-ters lift-ed me, Now safe am I.
Mer-its my soul's best songs; Faith-ful, lov-ing serv-ice, too, To Him be-longs.
Bil-lows His will o-bey; He your Sav-ior wants to be—Be saved to-day.

CHORUS

Love lift-ed me! . . . . Love lift-ed me! . . . . When noth-ing
e-ven me! e-ven me!

1.
else could help, Love lift-ed me.
2.
Love lift-ed me. A-MEN.

181 CALVARY COVERS IT ALL

Mrs. W. G. T.   Mrs. Walter G. Taylor

1. Far dear-er than all that the world can im-part Was the mes-sage tha
2. The stripes that He bore and the thorns that He wore Told His mer-cy and
3. How matchless the grace, when I looked in the face Of this Je-sus, my
4. How bless-ed the tho't, that my soul by Him bought, Shall be His in the

came to my heart (to my heart); How that Je-sus a-lone for my
love ev-er-more (ev-er-more); And my heart bowed in shame as I
cru-ci-fied Lord (of my Lord); My re-demp-tion com-plete I then
glo-ry on high (His on high), Where with gladness and song I'll be

sin did a-tone, And Cal-va-ry cov-ers it all. . . . . .
called on His name, And Cal-va-ry cov-ers it all. . . . . .
found at His feet, And Cal-va-ry cov-ers it all. . . . .
one of the throng, And Cal-va-ry cov-ers it all. . .
             cov-ers it all.

Chorus

Cal-va-ry cov-ers it all, . . My past with its sin and stain; My

guilt and de-spair Je-sus took on Him there, And Cal-va-ry cov-ers it all.

Inspired by the testimony of Charles Crawford, American Bible Society

182 SUNRISE

W. C. Poole   B. D. Ackley

1. When I shall come to the end of my way, When I shall rest at the
2. When in His beau-ty I see the great King, Join with the ran-somed His
3. When life is o - ver and day-light is passed, In heav-en's har-bor my

close of life's day, When "Wel-come home" I shall hear Je - sus say, O
prais-es to sing, When I shall join them my trib-utes to bring, O
an - chor is cast, When I see Je - sus my Sav - ior at last, O

that will be sun-rise for me. . . . . Sun-rise to-mor-row, sun-rise to-

mor-row, Sun-rise in glo-ry is wait-ing for me; Sun-rise to-mor-row,

sun-rise to - mor-row, Sun-rise with Je - sus for e - ter - ni - ty.

183 THE HAVEN OF REST

H. L. Gilmour

George D. Moore

1. My soul in sad ex - ile was out on life's sea, So bur-dened with
2. I yield-ed my-self to His ten-der em-brace, And faith tak-ing
3. The song of my soul, since the Lord made me whole, Has been the old
4. How pre-cious the tho't that we all may re-cline, Like John the be-
5. O come to the Sav-iour, He pa-tient-ly waits To save by His

sin and dis-tressed, Till I heard a sweet voice say-ing, "Make Me your choice;"
hold of the Word, My fet-ters fell off, and I an-chored my soul;
sto-ry so blest, Of Je-sus who'll save who-so-ev-er will have
lov-ed and blest, On Je-sus' strong arm, where no tem-pest can harm,
pow-er di-vine; Come, an-chor your soul in the "Ha-ven of Rest,"

CHORUS

And I en-tered the "Ha-ven of Rest."
The "Ha-ven of Rest" is my Lord.
A home in the "Ha-ven of Rest." I've an-chored my soul in the
Se-cure in the "Ha-ven of Rest."
And say, "My Be-lov-ed is mine."

"Ha-ven of Rest," I'll sail the wide seas no more; The tem-pest may

sweep o'er the wild storm-y deep; In Je-sus I'm safe ev-er-more.

184 WONDERFUL POWER

E. E. Hewitt

Chas. H. Gabriel

1. Won-der-ful pow'r of my won-der-ful King! Mer-cy un-
2. Won-der-ful pow'r of the prayer-hear-ing Lord; Tri-als a-
3. Won-der-ful pow'r that will guide me a-right, Lead me from
4. A-ble and will-ing, O Sav-ior, art Thou! A-ble and

bound-ed, I grate-ful-ly sing; From all the bil-lows that
claim on His grace will af-ford; On my dear Sav-ior I
shad-ows to mar-vel-ous light; In fierce temp-ta-tions, my
will-ing to save me just now; When earth-ly path-ways no

round me may roll, A-ble and will-ing to res-cue my soul.
cast ev-'ry care, A-ble and will-ing to an-swer my prayer.
ref-uge and stay, A-ble and will-ing to keep me each day.
lon-ger I roam, A-ble and will-ing to wel-come me home.

CHORUS

Won-der-ful pow'r, won-der-ful pow'r! Sav-ing me, keep-ing me, life's ev-'ry hour;

Glad-ly I sing, trust-ful-ly sing, Won-der-ful pow'r of my won-der-ful King.

185 SING AND SMILE AND PRAY THE CLOUDS AWAY

COPYRIGHT, 1934, BY HOMER A. RODEHEAVER
INTERNATIONAL COPYRIGHT SECURED

Written by The Brocks

1. Sing the clouds a - way, night will turn to day; If you sing and
2. Smile the clouds a - way, night will turn to day; If you smile and
4. Sing and smile and pray, that's the on - ly way; If you sing and

FINE.

sing and sing, You'll sing the clouds a - way.
smile and smile, You'll smile the clouds a - way.   3. Pray the clouds a - way,
smile and pray, You'll drive the clouds a - way.

D. C. 4th Verse

Pray and pray and pray; Night will turn to day, No mat - ter what they say.

186 LOST, BUT JESUS FOUND ME

A. P.

COPYRIGHT, 1934, BY HOMER A. RODEHEAVER
INTERNATIONAL COPYRIGHT SECURED

A. Phipps

Lost, but Je - sus found me; Blind, but now I see;

rit.

Bound, but, hal - le - lu - jah! Christ has set me free.

187 MORE LOVE TO THEE

Elizabeth Prentiss

W. H. Doane

1. More love to Thee, O Christ, More love to Thee! Hear Thou the
2. Once earth-ly joy I craved, Sought peace and rest; Now Thee a-
3. Then shall my lat-est breath Whis-per Thy praise; This be the

prayer I make On bend-ed knee; This is my ear-nest plea:
lone I seek, Give what is best; This all my prayer shall be:
part-ing cry My heart shall raise; This still its prayer shall be:

More love, O Christ, to Thee, More love to Thee, More love to Thee!

188 AMAZING GRACE

John Newton

1. A - maz-ing grace! how sweet the sound, That saved a wretch like me! I
2. 'Twas grace that taught my heart to fear, And grace my fears re-lieved; How
3. Thru man-y dan-gers, toils and snares, I have al-read-y come; 'Tis
4. When we've been there ten thousand years, Bright shin-ing as the sun, We've

once was lost, but now am found, Was blind, but now I see.
pre - cious did that grace ap-pear The hour I first be-lieved!
grace hath bro't me safe thus far, And grace will lead me home.
no less days to sing God's praise Than when we first be-gun. A-MEN.

189 JESUS NEVER FAILS

A. A. Luther

A. A. Luther

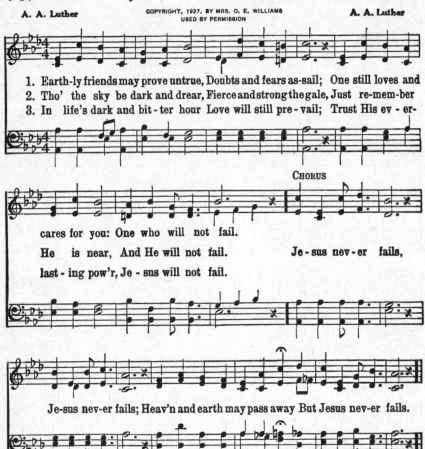

1. Earth-ly friends may prove untrue, Doubts and fears as-sail; One still loves and
2. Tho' the sky be dark and drear, Fierce and strong the gale, Just re-mem-ber
3. In life's dark and bit-ter hour Love will still pre-vail; Trust His ev-er-

CHORUS

cares for you: One who will not fail.

He is near, And He will not fail.   Je-sus nev-er fails,

last-ing pow'r, Je-sus will not fail.

Je-sus nev-er fails; Heav'n and earth may pass away But Jesus nev-er fails.

190 WHEN WE ALL GET TO HEAVEN

E. E. Hewitt

Mrs. J. G. Wilson

1. Sing the wondrous love of Je-sus, Sing His mer-cy and His grace;
2. While we walk the pil-grim path-way, Clouds will o-ver-spread the sky;
3. Let us then be true and faith-ful, Trust-ing, serv-ing ev-'ry day;
4. On-ward to the prize be-fore us! Soon His beau-ty we'll be-hold;

WHEN WE ALL GET TO HEAVEN

In the mansions bright and blessed, He'll prepare for us a place.
But when trav'ling days are o - ver, Not a shad-ow, not a sigh.
Just one glimpse of Him in glo - ry Will the toils of life re - pay.
Soon the pearl - y gates will o - pen, We shall tread the streets of gold.

for us a place.

CHORUS.

When we all get to heaven, What a day of rejoicing that will be!
When we all What a day of rejoicing that will be!

When we all see Jesus, We'll sing and shout the victory........
When we all and shout the vic-to-ry.

191 INTO MY HEART
(MY PRAYER)

H. D. C.
Sing Prayerfully

Harry D. Clarke

In - to my heart, In - to my heart, Come in - to my heart, Lord Je - sus;

Come in to-day, Come in to stay, Come in - to my heart, Lord, Je - sus.

192 O LOVE THAT WILT NOT LET ME GO

Rev. Geo. Matheson COPYRIGHT, 1938, RENEWAL. THE RODEHEAVER CO., OWNER J. B. Herbert

May be sung as Duet, Sop. & Tenor

1. O Love that wilt not let me go, I rest my wea-ry soul in Thee;
2. O Light that fol-low'st all my way, I yield my flick-'ring torch to Thee;
3. O Joy that seek-est me thro' pain, I can-not close my heart to Thee;
4. O Cross that lift-est up my head, I dare not ask to fly from Thee;

I give Thee back the life I owe, That in Thine o-cean depths its
My heart re-stores its bor-rowed ray, That in Thy sun-shine's glow its
I trace the rain-bow thro' the rain, And feel the prom-ise is not
I lay in dust life's glo-ry dead, And from the ground there blos-soms

flow May rich-er, full-er be, May rich-er, full-er be.
day May bright-er, fair-er be, May bright-er, fair-er be.
vain That morn shall tear-less be, That morn shall tear-less be.
red Life that shall end-less be, Life that shall end-less be.

193 LET THE BEAUTY OF JESUS

Affectionately dedicated to my friend, Gipsy Smith, as a token of appreciation for his loyal friendship thru many years.—B. D. A.

Albert Osborn COPYRIGHT, 1943, BY THE RODEHEAVER COMPANY B. D. Ackley

Let the beau-ty of Je-sus be seen in me (in me), All His

won-der-ful pas-sion and pu-ri-ty; O Thou Spir-it di-vine, All my

LET THE BEAUTY OF JESUS

rall.

na-ture re-fine Till the beau-ty of Je-sus my Sav-iour be seen in me.

NOTE:—Use of former melody forbidden by copyright restrictions, thus a new setting.

194   WONDERFUL WORDS OF LIFE

P. P. B.

P. P. Bliss

1. Sing them o-ver a-gain to me, Won-der-ful words of Life;
2. Christ, the bless-ed One, gives to all, Won-der-ful words of Life;
3. Sweet-ly ech-o the gos-pel call, Won-der-ful words of Life;

Let me more of their beau-ty see, Won-der-ful words of Life;
Sin-ner, list to the lov-ing call, Won-der-ful words of Life;
Of-fer par-don and peace to all, Won-der-ful words of Life;

Words of life and beau-ty, Teach me faith and du-ty:
All so free-ly giv-en, Woo-ing us to heav-en:
Je-sus, on-ly Sav-ior, Sanc-ti-fy for-ev-er:

REFRAIN

Beau-ti-ful words, won-der-ful words, Won-der-ful words of Life.   Life.

195 HE ROLLED THE SEA AWAY

Rev. H. J. Zelley

H. L. Gilmour

1. When Is-rael out of bond-age came, A sea be-fore them lay;
2. Be-fore me was a sea of sin, So great I feared to pray;
3. When sor-rows dark, like storm-y waves, Were dash-ing o'er my way,
4. And when I reach the sea of death, For need-ed grace I'll pray;

My Lord reached down His might-y hand, And rolled the sea a-way.
My heart's de-sire the Sav-ior read, And rolled the sea a-way.
A-gain the Lord in mer-cy came, And rolled the sea a-way.
I know the Lord will quick-ly come, And roll the sea a-way.

CHORUS

Then for-ward still, 'tis Je-ho-vah's will, Tho' the bil-lows dash and spray;

With a con-qu'ring tread we will push a-head, He'll roll the sea a-way.

196 YOUR CROSS

Martha E. Keck
With feeling

William M. Runyan

1. O Christian friend, do not de-spair Be-cause a cross you have to bear;
2. Re-mem-ber Christ on Cal-va-ry, The cross He bore for you and me;
3. Your heart with sorrow, too, must bleed, If you would be in word and deed
4. So, trusting heart, do not de-spair, Christ gives you strength your cross to bear;

YOUR CROSS

In ev - 'ry cross there is a gain, That sanc-ti-fies the deep-est pain.
Thru suff'ring there He now can share With sym-pa-thy your ev - 'ry care.
A com-fort to the troubled heart, And love and grace thru Him im-part.
Do not for-get, He is your Friend; He will a-bide un-to the end.

197   WHAT A FRIEND

Joseph Scriven   Charles C. Converse

1. What a Friend we have in Je - sus, All our sins and griefs to bear!
2. Have we tri - als and temp-ta - tions? Is there trou-ble an - y-where?
3. Are we weak and heav - y - la - den, Cumbered with a load of care?—

What a priv - i - lege to car - ry Ev - 'ry-thing to God in prayer!
We should nev-er be dis - cour-aged, Take it to the Lord in prayer.
Pre - cious Sav-iour, still our ref - uge,— Take it to the Lord in prayer.

O what peace we oft - en for - feit, O what need-less pain we bear,
Can we find a friend so faith - ful Who will all our sor-rows share?
Do thy friends de-spise, for-sake thee? Take it to the Lord in prayer;

All be-cause we do not car - ry Ev - 'ry-thing to God in prayer!
Je - sus knows our ev - 'ry weak-ness, Take it to the Lord in prayer.
In His arms He'll take and shield thee, Thou wilt find a sol - ace there.

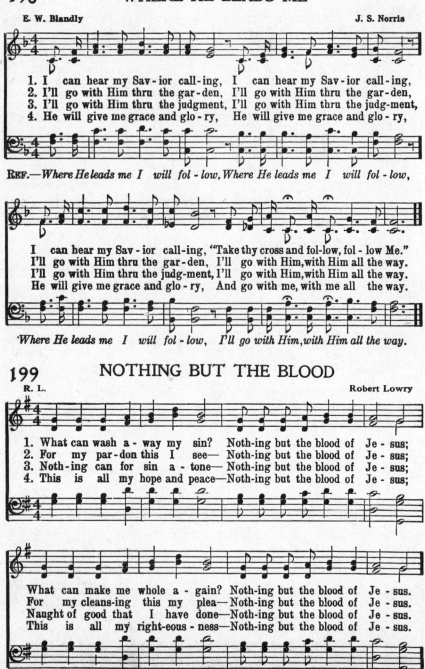

198 WHERE HE LEADS ME

E. W. Blandly

J. S. Norris

1. I can hear my Sav-ior call-ing, I can hear my Sav-ior call-ing,
2. I'll go with Him thru the gar-den, I'll go with Him thru the gar-den,
3. I'll go with Him thru the judgment, I'll go with Him thru the judg-ment,
4. He will give me grace and glo-ry, He will give me grace and glo-ry,

REF.—*Where He leads me I will fol-low, Where He leads me I will fol-low,*

I can hear my Sav-ior call-ing, "Take thy cross and fol-low, fol-low Me."
I'll go with Him thru the gar-den, I'll go with Him, with Him all the way.
I'll go with Him thru the judg-ment, I'll go with Him, with Him all the way.
He will give me grace and glo-ry, And go with me, with me all the way.

Where He leads me I will fol-low, I'll go with Him, with Him all the way.

199 NOTHING BUT THE BLOOD

R. L.

Robert Lowry

1. What can wash a-way my sin? Noth-ing but the blood of Je-sus;
2. For my par-don this I see— Noth-ing but the blood of Je-sus;
3. Noth-ing can for sin a-tone— Noth-ing but the blood of Je-sus;
4. This is all my hope and peace—Noth-ing but the blood of Je-sus;

What can make me whole a-gain? Noth-ing but the blood of Je-sus.
For my cleans-ing this my plea— Noth-ing but the blood of Je-sus.
Naught of good that I have done—Noth-ing but the blood of Je-sus.
This is all my right-eous-ness—Noth-ing but the blood of Je-sus.

NOTHING BUT THE BLOOD

REFRAIN

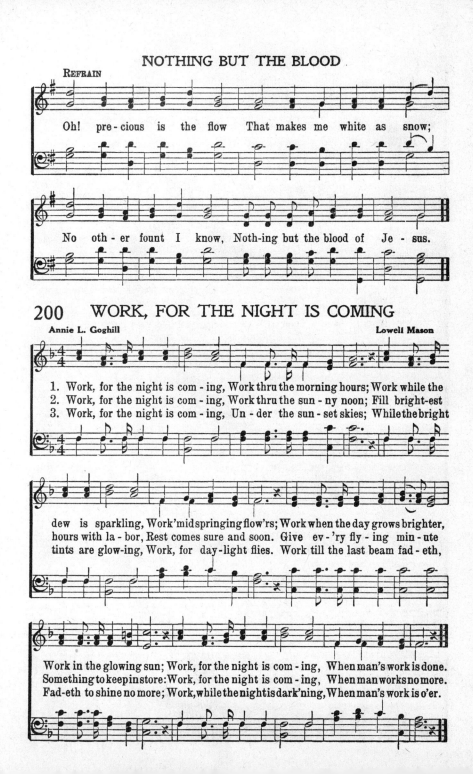

Oh! pre - cious is the flow That makes me white as snow;

No oth - er fount I know, Noth-ing but the blood of Je - sus.

200 WORK, FOR THE NIGHT IS COMING

Annie L. Goghill

Lowell Mason

1. Work, for the night is com - ing, Work thru the morning hours; Work while the
2. Work, for the night is com - ing, Work thru the sun - ny noon; Fill bright-est
3. Work, for the night is com - ing, Un - der the sun - set skies; While the bright

dew is sparkling, Work 'mid springing flow'rs; Work when the day grows brighter,
hours with la - bor, Rest comes sure and soon. Give ev - 'ry fly - ing min - ute
tints are glow-ing, Work, for day-light flies. Work till the last beam fad - eth,

Work in the glowing sun; Work, for the night is com - ing, When man's work is done.
Something to keep in store: Work, for the night is com - ing, When man works no more.
Fad-eth to shine no more; Work, while the night is dark'ning, When man's work is o'er.

201 THE OLD RUGGED CROSS

Rev. George Bennard   Rev. George Bennard

1. On a hill far a-way stood an old rug-ged cross, The em-blem of
2. Oh, the old rug-ged cross, so de-spised by the world, Has a wondrous at-
3. In the old rug-ged cross, stained with blood so di-vine, A won-drous
4. To the old rug-ged cross I will ev-er be true, Its shame and re-

suf-f'ring and shame; And I love that old cross where the dear-est and best
trac-tion for me; For the dear Lamb of God left His glo-ry a-bove
beau-ty I see; For 'twas on that old cross Je-sus suf-fered and died
proach gladly bear; Then He'll call me some day to my home far a-way,

For a world of lost sin-ners was slain.
To bear it to dark Cal-va-ry.
To par-don and sanc-ti-fy me.
Where His glo-ry for-ev-er I'll share.

CHORUS

So I'll cher-ish the old rug-ged cross, the
old rug-ged cross,

Till my tro-phies at last I lay down; I will cling to the

old rug-ged cross, And ex-change it some day for a crown.
cross, the old rug-ged cross,

202 JESUS, LOVER OF MY SOUL

(ABERYSTWYTH)

Charles Wesley

J. Parry, Mus. Doc.

1. Je - sus, Lov - er of my soul, Let me to Thy bo - som fly,
2. Oth - er ref - uge have I none, Hangs my help - less soul on Thee:
3. Thou, O Christ, art all I want; More than all in Thee I find;
4. Plen - teous grace with Thee is found, Grace to cov - er all my sin;

While the near - er wa - ters roll, While the tem - pest still is high!
Leave, O leave me not a - lone, Still sup - port and com - fort me:
Raise the fall - en, cheer the faint, Heal the sick, and lead the blind.
Let the heal - ing streams a - bound: Make and keep me pure with - in.

Hide me, O my Sav - ior, hide, Till the storm of life is past;
All my trust on Thee is stayed, All my help from Thee I bring;
Just and ho - ly is Thy name; I am all un - right - eous - ness:
Thou of life the foun - tain art, Free - ly let me take of Thee:

Safe in - to the ha - ven guide, O re - ceive my soul at last!
Cov - er my de - fense-less head With the shad - ow of Thy wing!
False and full of sin I am, Thou art full of truth and grace.
Spring Thou up with - in my heart, Rise to all e - ter - ni - ty.

RING THE BELLS OF HEAVEN

Rev. W. O. Cushing
G. F. Root

Joyfully

1. Ring the bells of heav-en! there is joy to-day, For a soul re-
2. Ring the bells of heav-en! there is joy to-day, For the wan-d'rer
3. Ring the bells of heav-en! spread the feast to-day! An-gels, swell the

turn-ing from the wild! See! the Fa-ther meets him out up-on the way,
now is rec-on-ciled; Yes, a soul is res-cued from his sin-ful way,
glad tri-um-phant strain! Tell the joy-ful ti-dings, bear it far a-way!

CHORUS

Wel-com-ing His wea-ry, wan-d'ring child.
And is born a-new a ran-somed child. Glo-ry! glo-ry! how the
For a pre-cious soul is born a-gain.

an-gels sing; Glo-ry! glo-ry! how the loud harps ring! 'Tis the ran-somed

ar-my, like a might-y sea, Peal-ing forth the an-them of the free.

STANDING ON THE PROMISES

R. K. C.

R. KELSO CARTER

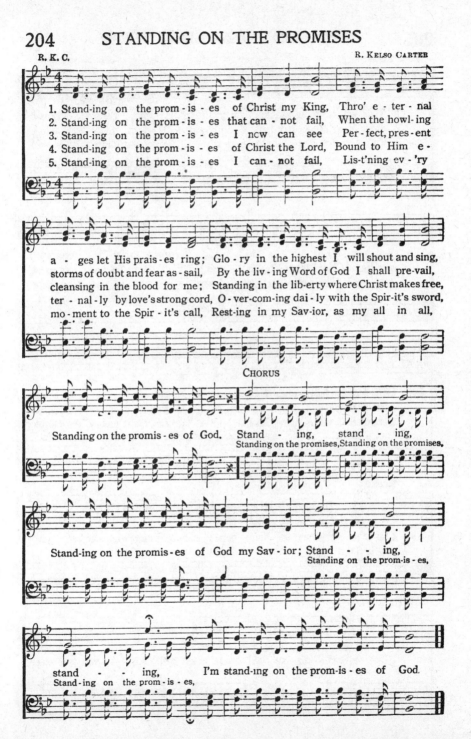

1. Stand-ing on the prom-is-es of Christ my King, Thro' e-ter-nal
2. Stand-ing on the prom-is-es that can-not fail, When the howl-ing
3. Stand-ing on the prom-is-es I now can see Per-fect, pres-ent
4. Stand-ing on the prom-is-es of Christ the Lord, Bound to Him e-
5. Stand-ing on the prom-is-es I can-not fail, Lis-t'ning ev-'ry

a - ges let His prais-es ring; Glo-ry in the highest I will shout and sing,
storms of doubt and fear as-sail, By the liv-ing Word of God I shall pre-vail,
cleansing in the blood for me; Standing in the lib-erty where Christ makes free,
ter-nal-ly by love's strong cord, O-ver-com-ing dai-ly with the Spir-it's sword,
mo-ment to the Spir-it's call, Rest-ing in my Sav-ior, as my all in all,

CHORUS

Standing on the promis-es of God. Stand - ing, stand - ing,
Standing on the promises, Standing on the promises,

Stand-ing on the promis-es of God my Sav-ior; Stand - - ing,
Standing on the prom-is-es,

stand - - ing, I'm stand-ing on the prom-is-es of God.
Stand-ing on the prom-is-es,

YIELD NOT TO TEMPTATION

206   TELL IT TO JESUS

J. E. Rankin, D. D.

E. S. Lorenz

1. Are you wea - ry, are you heav - y - heart - ed? Tell it to Je - sus,
2. Do the tears flow down your cheeks un - bid - den? Tell it to Je - sus,
3. Do you fear the gath-'ring clouds of sor - row? Tell it to Je - sus,
4. Are you troub - led at the tho't of dy - ing? Tell it to Je - sus,

Tell it to Je - sus; Are you griev - ing o - ver joys de - part - ed?
Tell it to Je - sus; Have you sins that to men's eyes are hid - den?
Tell it to Je - sus; Are you anx - ious what shall be to - mor - row?
Tell it to Je - sus; For Christ's com - ing King - dom are you sigh - ing?

CHORUS

Tell it to Je - sus a - lone. Tell it to Je - sus, Tell it to Je - sus,

He is a friend that's well - known; You've no oth - er

such a friend or broth - er, Tell it to Je - sus a - lone.

207 SAVIOR, LIKE A SHEPHERD LEAD US

DOROTHY ANN THRUPP

WILLIAM B. BRADBURY

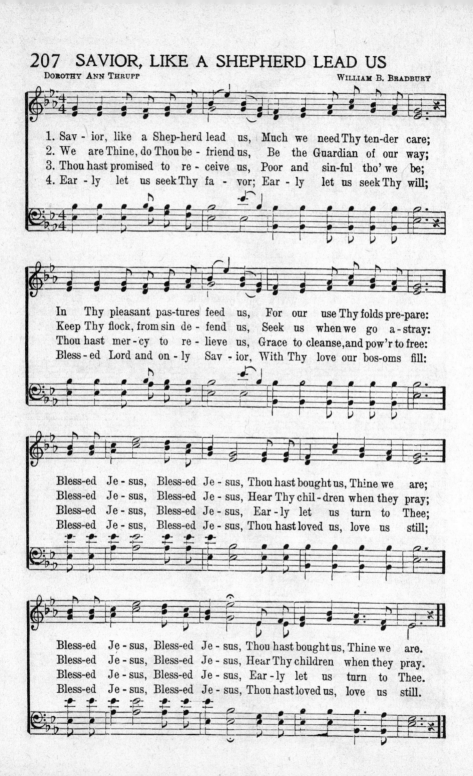

1. Sav - ior, like a Shep-herd lead us, Much we need Thy ten-der care;
2. We are Thine, do Thou be - friend us, Be the Guardian of our way;
3. Thou hast promised to re - ceive us, Poor and sin-ful tho' we be;
4. Ear - ly let us seek Thy fa - vor; Ear - ly let us seek Thy will;

In Thy pleasant pas-tures feed us, For our use Thy folds pre-pare:
Keep Thy flock, from sin de - fend us, Seek us when we go a - stray:
Thou hast mer - cy to re - lieve us, Grace to cleanse, and pow'r to free:
Bless - ed Lord and on - ly Sav - ior, With Thy love our bos-oms fill:

Bless-ed Je - sus, Bless-ed Je - sus, Thou hast bought us, Thine we are;
Bless-ed Je - sus, Bless-ed Je - sus, Hear Thy chil-dren when they pray;
Bless-ed Je - sus, Bless-ed Je - sus, Ear - ly let us turn to Thee;
Bless-ed Je - sus, Bless-ed Je - sus, Thou hast loved us, love us still;

Bless-ed Je - sus, Bless-ed Je - sus, Thou hast bought us, Thine we are.
Bless-ed Je - sus, Bless-ed Je - sus, Hear Thy children when they pray.
Bless-ed Je - sus, Bless-ed Je - sus, Ear - ly let us turn to Thee.
Bless-ed Je - sus, Bless-ed Je - sus, Thou hast loved us, love us still.

208 ABUNDANTLY ABLE TO SAVE

Elisha A. Hoffman

Philip P. Bliss

1. Who-ev-er re-ceiv-eth the Cru-ci-fied One, Who-ev-er be-liev-eth on
2. Who-ev-er re-ceiv-eth the mes-sage of God, And trusts in the pow'r of the
3. Who-ev-er re-pents and forsakes ev-'ry sin, And o-pens his heart for the

God's on-ly Son, A free and a per-fect sal-va-tion shall have:
soul-cleans-ing blood, A full and e-ter-nal re-demp-tion shall have:
Lord to come in, A pres-ent and per-fect sal-va-tion shall have:

FINE. CHORUS

For He is a-bun-dant-ly a-ble to save. My brother, the Mas-ter is
D.S.—And He is a-bun-dant-ly a-ble to save. Brother, the Master is

call-ing for thee; ... His grace and His mer-cy are won-drous-ly
come, and is call-ing for thee; Broth-er, His grace and His mer-cy are

D.S.

free; ... His blood as a ran-som for sin-ners He gave, ...
won-drous-ly free; Broth-er, His blood as a ran-som for sin-ners He gave,

209 SAFELY THROUGH ANOTHER WEEK

John Newton

Lowell Mason

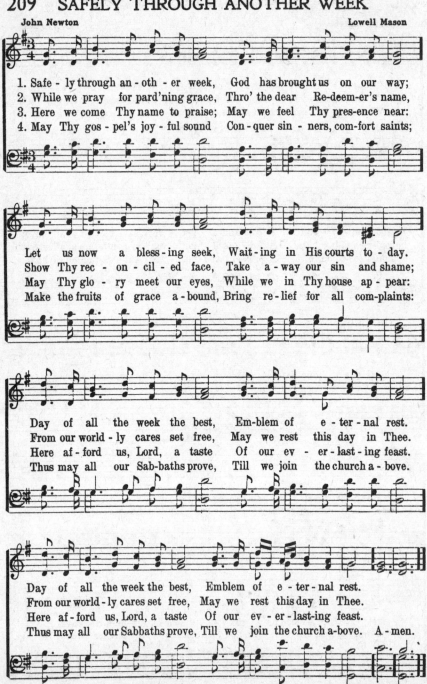

1. Safe - ly through an - oth - er week, God has brought us on our way;
2. While we pray for pard'ning grace, Thro' the dear Re-deem-er's name,
3. Here we come Thy name to praise; May we feel Thy pres-ence near:
4. May Thy gos - pel's joy - ful sound Con - quer sin - ners, com-fort saints;

Let us now a bless - ing seek, Wait - ing in His courts to - day.
Show Thy rec - on - cil - ed face, Take a - way our sin and shame;
May Thy glo - ry meet our eyes, While we in Thy house ap - pear:
Make the fruits of grace a - bound, Bring re - lief for all com-plaints:

Day of all the week the best, Em-blem of e - ter - nal rest.
From our world - ly cares set free, May we rest this day in Thee.
Here af - ford us, Lord, a taste Of our ev - er - last - ing feast.
Thus may all our Sab-baths prove, Till we join the church a - bove.

Day of all the week the best, Emblem of e - ter - nal rest.
From our world - ly cares set free, May we rest this day in Thee.
Here af - ford us, Lord, a taste Of our ev - er - last-ing feast.
Thus may all our Sabbaths prove, Till we join the church a-bove. A - men.

210 FACE TO FACE

Mrs. Frank A. Breck **Grant Colfax Tullar**

Moderato.

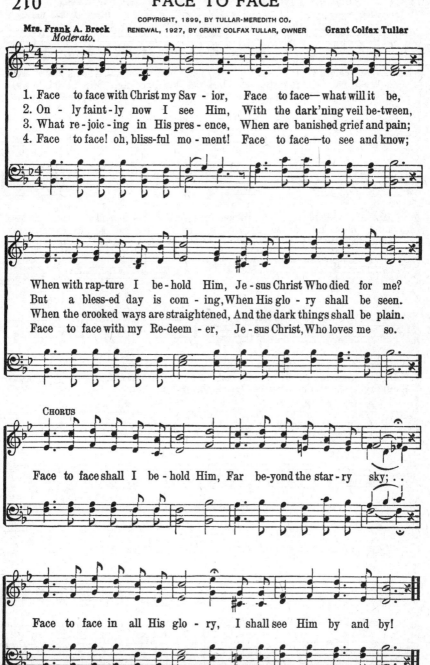

1. Face to face with Christ my Sav - ior, Face to face—what will it be,
2. On - ly faint-ly now I see Him, With the dark'ning veil be-tween,
3. What re-joic-ing in His pres-ence, When are banished grief and pain;
4. Face to face! oh, bliss-ful mo - ment! Face to face—to see and know;

When with rap-ture I be-hold Him, Je-sus Christ Who died for me?
But a bless-ed day is com-ing, When His glo-ry shall be seen.
When the crooked ways are straightened, And the dark things shall be plain.
Face to face with my Re-deem - er, Je-sus Christ, Who loves me so.

CHORUS

Face to face shall I be-hold Him, Far be-yond the star-ry sky; . .

Face to face in all His glo - ry, I shall see Him by and by!

211 GOOD NIGHT AND GOOD MORNING

Lizzie DeArmond   Homer A. Rodeheaver

1. When comes to the wea-ry a bless-ed re-lease, When upward we
2. When fad-eth the day and dark shadows draw nigh, With Christ close at
3. When home-lights we see shin-ing bright-ly a-bove, Where we shall be

pass to His kingdom of peace, When free from the woes that on earth we must bear,
hand, it is not death to die; He'll wipe ev-'ry tear, roll a-way ev-'ry care;
soon, thro' His wonderful love, We'll praise Him who called us His heaven to share,

CHORUS.

We'll say "good-night," here, but "good-morning" up there.
We'll say "good-night," here, but "good-morning" up there. Good morning up there where
We'll say "good-night," here, but "good-morning" up there.

Christ is the Light, Good-morning up there where cometh no night; When we step from this

earth to God's heaven so fair, We'll say "good-night" here, but "good-morning" up there.

212 O THAT WILL BE GLORY

C. H. G. Words and music CHAS. H. GABRIEL

1. When all my la-bors and tri-als are o'er, And I am safe on that
2. When, by the gift of His in-fi-nite grace, I am ac-cord-ed in
3. Friends will be there I have loved long a-go; Joy like a riv-er a-

beau-ti-ful shore, Just to be near the dear Lord I a-dore,
heav-en a place, Just to be there and to look on His face,
round me will flow; Yet, just a smile from my Sav-ior, I know,

Will thro' the a-ges be glo-ry for me.... O that will be
O............... that will

glo-ry for me, Glo-ry for me, glo-ry for me; When by His grace
be glo-ry for me, glo-ry for me, glo-ry for me;...........

I shall look on His face, That will be glo-ry, be glo-ry for me.

213 MORE LIKE THE MASTER

C. H. G.

Chas. H. Gabriel

1. More like the Mas-ter I would ev-er be, More of His meek-ness,
2. More like the Mas-ter is my dai-ly prayer; More strength to car-ry
3. More like the Mas-ter I would live and grow; More of His love to

more hu-mil-i-ty; More zeal to la-bor, more cour-age to be true,
cross-es I must bear; More ear-nest ef-fort to bring His kingdom in;
oth-ers I would show; More self-de-ni-al, like His in Gal-i-lee,

rit.

CHORUS

More con-se-cra-tion for work He bids me do. . . . Take Thou my
More of His Spir-it, the wan-der-er to win. . . .
More like the Mas-ter I long to ev-er be. . . . Take my heart, O

heart, . . I would be Thine a-lone; . . Take Thou my heart . . and
take my heart, I would be Thine a-lone; Take my heart, O take my heart and

make it all Thine own; . . Purge me from sin, ... O Lord, I now im-
make it all Thine own; Purge Thou me from ev-'ry sin, O Lord, I

MORE LIKE THE MASTER

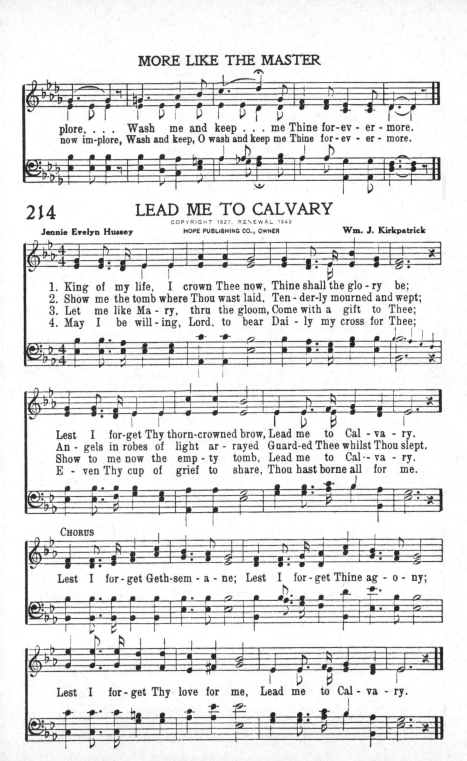

plore, . . . Wash me and keep . . . me Thine for-ev - er - more.
now im-plore, Wash and keep, O wash and keep me Thine for-ev - er - more.

214 LEAD ME TO CALVARY

COPYRIGHT 1921. RENEWAL 1949
HOPE PUBLISHING CO., OWNER

Jennie Evelyn Hussey   Wm. J. Kirkpatrick

1. King of my life, I crown Thee now, Thine shall the glo - ry be;
2. Show me the tomb where Thou wast laid, Ten - der-ly mourned and wept;
3. Let me like Ma - ry, thru the gloom, Come with a gift to Thee;
4. May I be will - ing, Lord, to bear Dai - ly my cross for Thee;

Lest I for-get Thy thorn-crowned brow, Lead me to Cal - va - ry.
An - gels in robes of light ar - rayed Guard-ed Thee whilst Thou slept.
Show to me now the emp - ty tomb, Lead me to Cal - va - ry.
E - ven Thy cup of grief to share, Thou hast borne all for me.

CHORUS

Lest I for-get Geth-sem - a - ne; Lest I for-get Thine ag - o - ny;

Lest I for-get Thy love for me, Lead me to Cal - va - ry.

215 SOME BRIGHT MORNING

Charlotte G. Homer

Chas. H. Gabriel

1. Be not a - wea - ry, for la - bor will cease Some glad morn-ing;
2. Wea - ri-some bur-dens will all be laid down, Some glad morn-ing;
3. La - bor well done shall re - ceive its re - ward, Some glad morn-ing;
4. O what a time of re - joic-ing will come, Some glad morn-ing;
5. There with the loved ones who've gone on be - fore, Some glad morn-ing;

Tur-moil will change in-to in - fi - nite peace, Some bright morn-ing.
Then shall our cross be exchanged for a crown, Some bright morn-ing.
Thou who art faith-ful shall be with the Lord, Some bright morn-ing.
When all the ransomed are gathered at home, Some bright morn-ing.
We shall sing praise to the Lamb ev - er - more, Some bright morn-ing.

CHORUS

Some bright morn-ing, Some glad morn-ing, When the sun is shin-ing in th' e-ter - nal sky; . . . Some bright morn-ing, Some glad morn-ing, We shall see the Lord of Har-vest, By and by.

216 GOD'S TOMORROW

A. H. A.

A. H. Ackley

1. God's tomorrow is a day of gladness, And its joys shall nev-er fade;
2. God's tomorrow is a day of greeting: We shall see the Savior's face;
3. God's tomorrow is a day of glo - ry: We shall wear the crown of life;

No more weeping, no more sense of sad-ness, No more foes to make a - fraid.
And our longing hearts a-wait the meeting In that ho - ly, hap-py place.
Sing thro' countless years love's old, old story, Free for-ev - er from all strife.

REFRAIN.

God's to - mor - row, God's to-mor - row, Ev - 'ry cloud will pass a-way

At the dawning of that day; God's to - mor - row, No more sor - row,

For I know that God's to - mor-row Will be better than to - day!

217 O BEULAH LAND

EDGAR PAGE

JNO. R. SWENEY

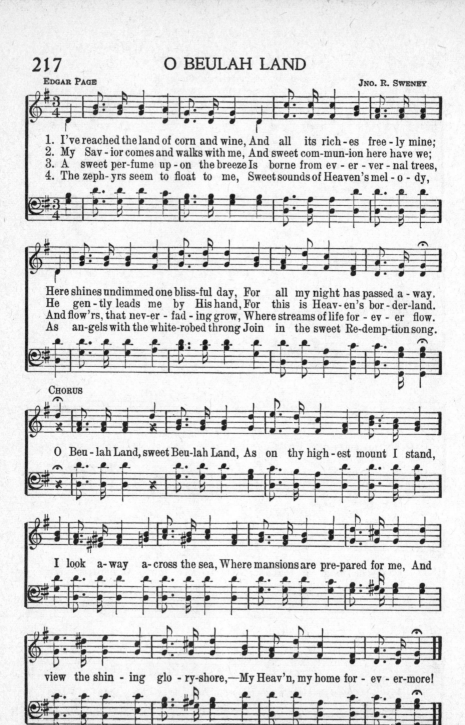

1. I've reached the land of corn and wine, And all its rich-es free-ly mine;
2. My Sav-ior comes and walks with me, And sweet com-mun-ion here have we;
3. A sweet per-fume up-on the breeze Is borne from ev-er-ver-nal trees,
4. The zeph-yrs seem to float to me, Sweet sounds of Heaven's mel-o-dy,

Here shines undimmed one bliss-ful day, For all my night has passed a-way.
He gen-tly leads me by His hand, For this is Heav-en's bor-der-land.
And flow'rs, that nev-er-fad-ing grow, Where streams of life for-ev-er flow.
As an-gels with the white-robed throng Join in the sweet Re-demp-tion song.

CHORUS

O Beu-lah Land, sweet Beu-lah Land, As on thy high-est mount I stand,

I look a-way a-cross the sea, Where mansions are pre-pared for me, And

view the shin-ing glo-ry-shore,—My Heav'n, my home for-ev-er-more!

218 WHERE WE'LL NEVER GROW OLD

Dedicated to my Father and Mother

Jas. C. Moore

Jas. C. Moore

1. I have heard of a land on the far-a-way strand, 'Tis a
2. In that beau-ti-ful home where we'll nev-er-more roam, We shall
3. When our work here is done and the life-crown is won, And our

beau-ti-ful home of the soul; Built by Je-sus on high, there we
be in the sweet by and by; Hap-py praise to the King thro' e-
troub-les and tri-als are o'er, All our sor-row will end, and our

nev-er shall die, 'Tis a land where we nev-er grow old.
ter-ni-ty sing, 'Tis a land where we nev-er shall die.
voic-es will blend With the loved ones who've gone on be-fore.

CHORUS

Nev-er grow old, nev-er grow old, In a land where we'll never grow old;

Where we'll

Nev-er grow old, nev-er grow old, In a land where we'll never grow old.

Where we'll

THE KINGDOM IS COMING

Mary B. C. Slade

Robert M. McIntosh

1. From all the dark pla - ces Of earth's hea-then ra - ces, O
2. The sun - light is glanc - ing O'er ar - mies ad - vanc - ing To
3. With shout - ing and sing - ing, And ju - bi-lant ring - ing, Their

see how the thick shadows fly! The voice of sal - va - tion A -
con - quer the king - doms of sin; Our Lord shall pos-sess them, His
arms of re - bel - lion cast down, At last ev - 'ry na - tion, The

wakes ev - 'ry na - tion, "Come o - ver and help us," they cry.
pres - ence shall bless them, His beau - ty shall en - ter them in.
Lord of sal - va - tion Their King and Re - deem - er shall crown!

REFRAIN

The kingdom is coming, O tell ye the story, God's banner ex-alt-ed shall be!

The earth shall be full of His knowledge and glory, As waters that cover the sea!

220 WE'VE A STORY TO TELL TO THE NATIONS

COLIN STERNE

H. ERNEST NICHOL

1. We've a sto - ry to tell to the na - tions That shall turn their hearts
2. We've a song to be sung to the na - tions That shall lift their hearts
3. We've a mes-sage to give to the na - tions, That the Lord who reign -
4. We've a Sav - ior to show to the na - tions Who the path of sor -

to the right, A sto - ry of truth and mer - cy, A
to the Lord, A song that shall con - quer e - vil And
eth a - bove Hath sent us His Son to save us, And
row hath trod, That all of the world's great peo - ples Might

sto - ry of peace and light, A sto - ry of peace and light.
shat - ter the spear and sword, And shat - ter the spear and sword.
show us that God is love, And show us that God is love.
come to the truth of God, Might come to the truth of God.

CHORUS

For the darkness shall turn to dawn-ing, And the dawning to noonday bright,

rall.

And Christ's great kingdom shall come to earth, The kingdom of love and light.

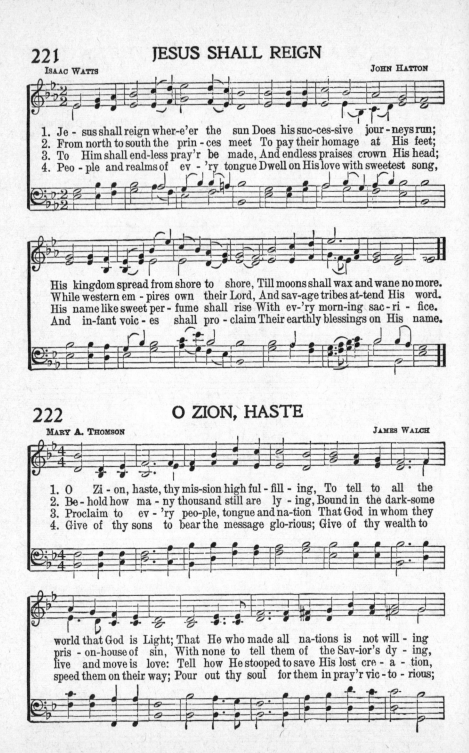

221

JESUS SHALL REIGN

Isaac Watts

John Hatton

1. Je - sus shall reign wher-e'er the sun Does his suc-ces-sive jour-neys run;
2. From north to south the prin - ces meet To pay their homage at His feet;
3. To Him shall end-less pray'r be made, And endless praises crown His head;
4. Peo - ple and realms of ev - 'ry tongue Dwell on His love with sweetest song,

His kingdom spread from shore to shore, Till moons shall wax and wane no more.
While western em - pires own their Lord, And sav-age tribes at-tend His word.
His name like sweet per - fume shall rise With ev-'ry morn-ing sac - ri - fice.
And in-fant voic - es shall pro - claim Their earthly blessings on His name.

222

O ZION, HASTE

Mary A. Thomson

James Walch

1. O Zi - on, haste, thy mis-sion high ful - fill - ing, To tell to all the
2. Be - hold how ma - ny thousand still are ly - ing, Bound in the dark-some
3. Proclaim to ev - 'ry peo-ple, tongue and na-tion That God in whom they
4. Give of thy sons to bear the message glo-rious; Give of thy wealth to

world that God is Light; That He who made all na-tions is not will - ing
pris - on-house of sin, With none to tell them of the Sav-ior's dy - ing,
live and move is love: Tell how He stooped to save His lost cre - a - tion,
speed them on their way; Pour out thy soul for them in pray'r vic - to - rious;

O ZION, HASTE

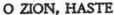

REFRAIN

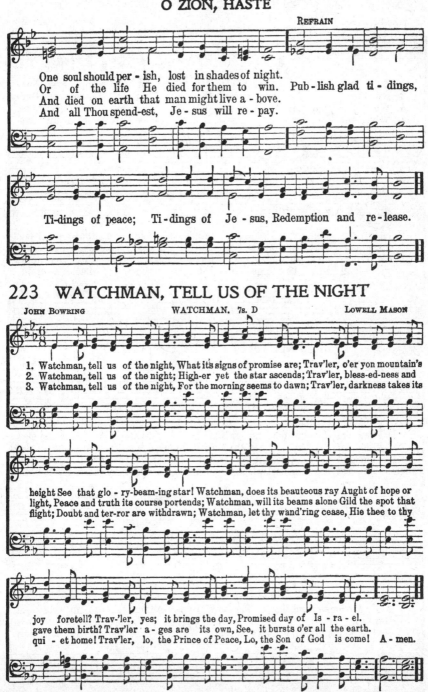

One soul should per-ish, lost in shades of night.
Or of the life He died for them to win. Pub-lish glad ti-dings,
And died on earth that man might live a-bove.
And all Thou spend-est, Je-sus will re-pay.

Ti-dings of peace; Ti-dings of Je-sus, Redemption and re-lease.

223 WATCHMAN, TELL US OF THE NIGHT

JOHN BOWRING

WATCHMAN. 7s. D

LOWELL MASON

1. Watchman, tell us of the night, What its signs of promise are; Trav'ler, o'er yon mountain's
2. Watchman, tell us of the night; High-er yet the star ascends; Trav'ler, bless-ed-ness and
3. Watchman, tell us of the night, For the morning seems to dawn; Trav'ler, darkness takes its

height See that glo-ry-beam-ing star! Watchman, does its beauteous ray Aught of hope or
light, Peace and truth its course portends; Watchman, will its beams alone Gild the spot that
flight; Doubt and ter-ror are withdrawn; Watchman, let thy wand'ring cease, Hie thee to thy

joy foretell? Trav-'ler, yes; it brings the day, Promised day of Is-ra-el.
gave them birth? Trav'ler a-ges are its own, See, it bursts o'er all the earth.
qui-et home! Trav'ler, lo, the Prince of Peace, Lo, the Son of God is come! A-men.

224

BLEST BE THE TIE

John Fawcett

Hans G. Naegeli

1. Blest be the tie that binds Our hearts in Chris-tian love; The
2. Be - fore our Fa-ther's throne We pour our ar - dent prayers; Our
3. We share our mu - tual woes, Our mu - tual bur - dens bear; And
4. When we a - sun - der part, It gives us in - ward pain; But

fel - low-ship of kin - dred minds Is like to that a - bove.
fears, our hopes, our aims are one, Our com-forts and our cares.
oft - en for each oth - er flows The sym - pa - thiz-ing tear.
we shall still be joined in heart, And hope to meet a - gain.

225

FLING OUT THE BANNER

George W. Doane

John B. Calkin

1. Fling out the ban-ner! let it float Sky-ward and sea-ward, high and wide;
2. Fling out the ban-ner! an-gels bend In anx-ious si-lence o'er the sign.
3. Fling out the ban-ner! hea-then lands Shall see from far the glo-rious sight;
4. Fling out the ban-ner! let it float Sky-ward and sea-ward, high and wide,
5. Fling out the ban-ner! wide and high, Sea-ward and sky-ward, let it shine;

The sun, that lights its shin-ing folds, The cross, on which the Sav - ior died.
And vain-ly seek to com-pre-hend The won-der of the love di-vine.
And na-tions crowd-ing to be born, Bap-tize their spir - its in its light.
Our glo - ry, on - ly in the cross; Our on - ly hope the Cru - ci - fied.
Nor skill, nor might, nor mer - it ours; We con - quer on - ly in that sign.

226 IN CHRIST THERE IS NO EAST OR WEST

John Oxenham

Alexander R. Reinagle

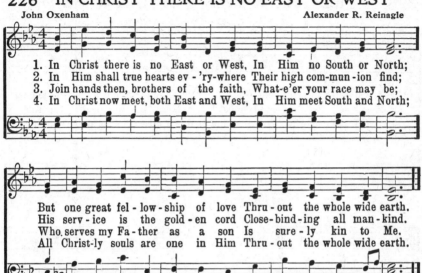

1. In Christ there is no East or West, In Him no South or North;
2. In Him shall true hearts ev - 'ry-where Their high com-mun-ion find;
3. Join hands then, brothers of the faith, What-e'er your race may be;
4. In Christ now meet, both East and West, In Him meet South and North;

But one great fel - low-ship of love Thru-out the whole wide earth.
His serv - ice is the gold - en cord Close-bind-ing all man-kind.
Who. serves my Fa - ther as a son Is sure-ly kin to Me.
All Christ-ly souls are one in Him Thru-out the whole wide earth.

227 WHERE CROSS THE CROWDED WAYS OF LIFE

F. MASON NORTH

BEETHOVEN

1. Where cross the crowded ways of life, Where sounds the cries of race and clan,
2. In haunts of wretch-ed - ness and need, On shadowed thresholds dark with fears,
3. The cup of wa - ter giv'n for Thee Still holds the freshness of Thy grace;
4. O Mas-ter, from the mountain side, Make haste to heal these hearts of pain,
5. Till sons of men shall learn Thy love And fol-low where Thy feet have trod:

A - bove the noise of self-ish strife, We hear Thy voice, O Son of man!
From paths where hide the lures of greed, We catch the vi - sion of Thy tears.
Yet long these mul - ti - tudes to see The sweet com-pas-sion of Thy face.
A - mong these restless throngs a-bide, O tread the cit - y's streets a-gain.
Till glo - rious from Thy heav'n above Shall come the cit - y of our God.

228 TILL THE WHOLE WORLD KNOWS

Rev. A. H. Ackley

B. D. Ackley

1. I'll tell to all that God is love; For the world has nev-er known
2. I'll tell of mer-cy's boundless tide, Like the wa-ters of the sea,
3. I'll tell of grace that keeps the soul, Of a-bid-ing peace with-in,
4. E-ter-nal glo-ry is the goal That a-waits the sons of light;

The great com-pas-sion of His heart For the wayward and the lone.
That cov-ers ev-'ry sin of man; 'Tis sal-va-tion full and free.
Of faith that o-ver-comes the world, With its tu-mult and its din.
E-ter-nal dark-ness, black as death, For the children of the night.

CHORUS.

Till the whole world knows, Till the whole world
Till the world, till the whole world knows, Till the world, till the whole world,

Till the world, the whole world knows,

knows, I will shout and sing Of Christ my King, Till the whole world knows.
whole world knows,

229
THE END OF THE ROAD

(Dedicated to Evangelist Harry W. Vom Bruch)

Lizzie DeArmond   **Elton M. Roth**

1. When I come to the end of the long, long road, The shad-ows will
2. Look-ing back o'er the years that were hard and drear, The hand of the
3. When I come to the end of the long, long road, And tri-als will

flee a-way, And I'll stand in the glo-ri-ous light of God,
will flee a-way,
Christ I'll see; While my heart will go forth with a song of praise,
the Christ I'll see;
all be past, I shall look in the face of my dear-est Friend,
will all be past,

CHORUS

Where dwell-eth e-ter-nal day.... When I come to the end, the
Be-cause of His love for me....
Safe home in His heav'n at last.... When I come to the

end of the road, To the land of e-ter-ni-ty, When I
To the land of e-ter-ni-ty,

rit.

come to the end of life's long road, The face of my Lord I'll see.

230   O LITTLE TOWN OF BETHLEHEM

PHILLIPS BROOKS

LEWIS H. REDNER

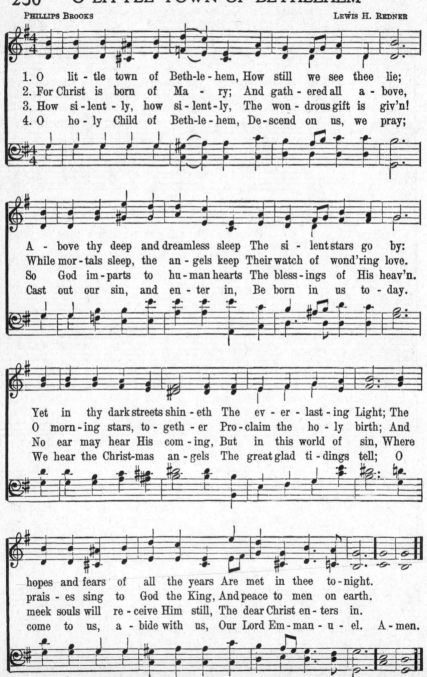

1. O lit-tle town of Beth-le-hem, How still we see thee lie;
2. For Christ is born of Ma-ry; And gath-ered all a-bove,
3. How si-lent-ly, how si-lent-ly, The won-drous gift is giv'n!
4. O ho-ly Child of Beth-le-hem, De-scend on us, we pray;

A-bove thy deep and dreamless sleep The si-lent stars go by:
While mor-tals sleep, the an-gels keep Their watch of wond'ring love.
So God im-parts to hu-man hearts The bless-ings of His heav'n.
Cast out our sin, and en-ter in, Be born in us to-day.

Yet in thy dark streets shin-eth The ev-er-last-ing Light; The
O morn-ing stars, to-geth-er Pro-claim the ho-ly birth; And
No ear may hear His com-ing, But in this world of sin, Where
We hear the Christ-mas an-gels The great glad ti-dings tell; O

hopes and fears of all the years Are met in thee to-night.
prais-es sing to God the King, And peace to men on earth.
meek souls will re-ceive Him still, The dear Christ en-ters in.
come to us, a-bide with us, Our Lord Em-man-u-el. A-men.

231 JOY TO THE WORLD!

Isaac Watts   George F. Handel

1. Joy to the world! the Lord is come; Let earth re-
2. Joy to the earth! the Sav-ior reigns; Let men their
3. No more let sins and sor-rows grow, Nor thorns in-
4. He rules the world with truth and grace, And makes the

ceive her King; Let ev-'ry heart pre-pare Him room,
songs em-ploy; While fields and floods, rocks, hills and plains
fest the ground; He comes to make His bless-ings flow
na-tions prove The glo-ries of His right-eous-ness,

And heav'n and na-ture sing, And heav'n and na-ture
Re-peat the sound-ing joy, Re-peat the sound-ing
Far as the curse is found, Far as the curse is
And won-ders of His love, And won-ders of His

1. And heav'n and na-ture sing, ... And

sing, And heav'n, and heav'n and na-ture sing.
joy, Re-peat, re-peat the sound-ing joy.
found, Far as, far as the curse is found.
love, And won-ders, and won-ders of His love.

heav'n and na-ture sing,

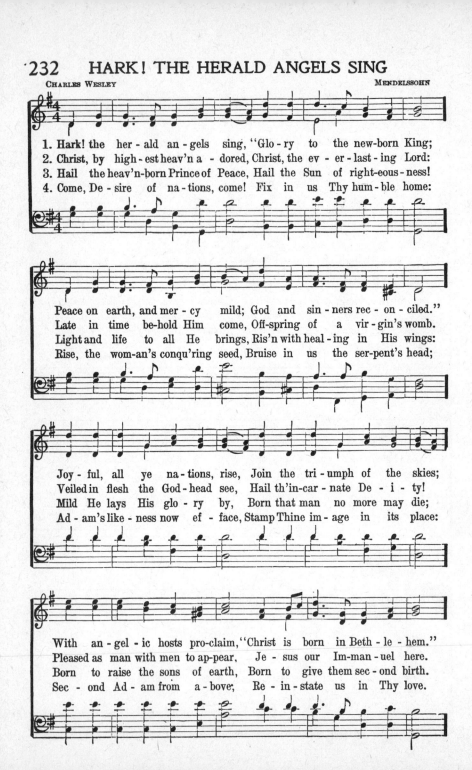

232 HARK! THE HERALD ANGELS SING

Charles Wesley

Mendelssohn

1. Hark! the her-ald an-gels sing, "Glo-ry to the new-born King;
2. Christ, by high-est heav'n a-dored, Christ, the ev-er-last-ing Lord:
3. Hail the heav'n-born Prince of Peace, Hail the Sun of right-eous-ness!
4. Come, De-sire of na-tions, come! Fix in us Thy hum-ble home:

Peace on earth, and mer-cy mild; God and sin-ners rec-on-ciled."
Late in time be-hold Him come, Off-spring of a vir-gin's womb.
Light and life to all He brings, Ris'n with heal-ing in His wings:
Rise, the wom-an's conqu'ring seed, Bruise in us the ser-pent's head;

Joy-ful, all ye na-tions, rise, Join the tri-umph of the skies;
Veiled in flesh the God-head see, Hail th'in-car-nate De-i-ty!
Mild He lays His glo-ry by, Born that man no more may die;
Ad-am's like-ness now ef-face, Stamp Thine im-age in its place:

With an-gel-ic hosts pro-claim, "Christ is born in Beth-le-hem."
Pleased as man with men to ap-pear, Je-sus our Im-man-uel here.
Born to raise the sons of earth, Born to give them sec-ond birth.
Sec-ond Ad-am from a-bove, Re-in-state us in Thy love.

HARK! THE HERALD ANGELS SING

Hark! the her - ald an-gels sing, "Glo - ry to the new-born King." Amen.

233   O COME, ALL YE FAITHFUL

Tr. by FREDERICK OAKELEY

WADE'S Cantus Diversi

1. O come, all ye faith - ful, joy - ful and tri - um-phant, O
2. Sing, choirs of an - gels, sing in ex - ul - ta - tion, O
3. Yea, Lord, we greet Thee, born this hap - py morn-ing,

come ye, O come ye to Beth - le - hem; Come and be - hold Him,
sing, all ye bright hosts of heav'n a - bove; Glo - ry to God, all
Je - sus, to Thee be all glo - ry giv'n; Word of the Fa - ther,

REFRAIN

born the King of an - gels.
glo - ry in the high - est. O come, let us a - dore Him, O come, let us a-
now in flesh ap - pear-ing.

dore Him, O come, let us a - dore Him, Christ, the Lord. A - men.

234 THE FIRST NOEL

Traditional   Traditional

1. The first No - el the an - gel did say Was to cer - tain poor
2. And by the light of that same Star, Three wise men
3. This Star drew nigh to the north - west, O'er Beth - le -
4. Then en - tered in, those wise men three, Full rev - 'rent -

shep-herds in fields as they lay; In fields where they lay keep-ing their
came from coun - try far; To seek for a King was their in -
hem it took its rest, And there it did both stop and
ly up - on their knee, And of - fered there in His pres -

REFRAIN

sheep, On a cold win - ter's night that was so deep.
tent, And to fol - low the Star wher - ev - er it went. No - el, No -
stay, Right o - ver the place where Je - sus lay.
ence, Their gold, and myrrh, and frank - in - cense.

el, No - el, No - el, Born is the King of Is - - ra - el.

235 SILENT NIGHT

Joseph Mohr   P. M.   Franz Gruber

1. Si - lent night! ho - ly night! All is calm, all is bright 'Round yon
2. Si - lent night! ho - ly night! Shep - herds quake at the sight! Glo - ries
3. Si - lent night! ho - ly night! Son of God, love's pure light Ra - diant

SILENT NIGHT

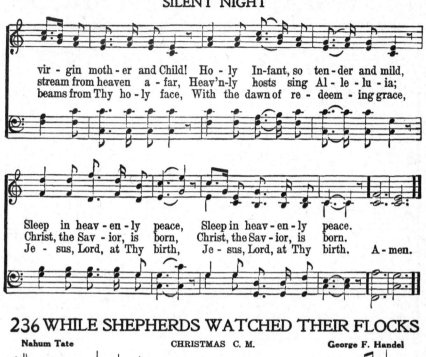

vir - gin moth - er and Child! Ho - ly In-fant, so ten - der and mild,
stream from heaven a - far, Heav'n-ly hosts sing Al - le - lu - ia;
beams from Thy ho - ly face, With the dawn of re - deem - ing grace,

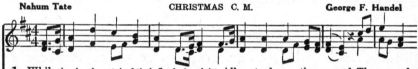

Sleep in heav - en - ly peace, Sleep in heav - en - ly peace.
Christ, the Sav - ior, is born, Christ, the Sav - ior, is born.
Je - sus, Lord, at Thy birth, Je - sus, Lord, at Thy birth. A - men.

236 WHILE SHEPHERDS WATCHED THEIR FLOCKS

Nahum Tate CHRISTMAS C. M. **George F. Handel**

1. While shepherds watched their flocks by night, All seat-ed on the ground, The an-gel
2. "Fear not," said he; for might-y dread Had seized their troubled mind, "Glad tidings
3. "To you, in Da-vid's town, this day Is born, of Da-vid's line, The Sav-ior,
4. "The heav'nly Babe you there shall find To hu-man view dis-played, All mean-ly
5. "All glo-ry be to God on high, And to the earth be peace; Good-will hence-

of the Lord came down, And glory shone a-round, And glo-ry shone a-round.
of great joy I bring, To you and all mankind, To you and all mankind.
who is Christ the Lord; And this shall be the sign, And this shall be the sign:
wrapped in swathing bands, And in a man-ger laid, And in a man-ger laid."
forth from heav'n to men Be-gin, and never cease, Be-gin, and never cease!" AMEN.

237 CHRIST, THE LORD, IS RISEN TODAY

Charles Wesley   (WORGAN)   From "Lyra Davidica"

1. Christ the Lord is ris'n to-day, Al - - le-lu - ia!
2. Lives a - gain our glo-rious King: Al - - le-lu - ia!
3. Love's re - deem-ing work is done, Al - - le-lu - ia!
4. Soar we now, where Christ has led, Al - - le-lu - ia!

Sons of men and an - gels say: Al - - le-lu - ia!
Where, O death, is now thy sting? Al - - le-lu - ia!
Fought the fight, the bat - tle won; Al - - le-lu - ia!
Fol - l'wing our ex - alt - ed Head; Al - - le-lu - ia!

Raise your joys and tri-umphs high, Al - - le-lu - ia!
Dy - ing once, He all doth save: Al - - le-lu - ia!
Death in vain for - bids Him rise; Al - - le-lu - ia!
Made like Him, like Him we rise; Al - - le-lu - ia!

Sing, ye heav'ns, and earth re - ply, Al - - le-lu - ia!
Where thy vic - to - ry, O grave? Al - - le-lu - ia!
Christ has o - pened Par - a - dise. Al - - le-lu - ia!
Ours the cross, the grave, the skies. Al - - le-lu - ia!

238 CHRIST AROSE

R. L.

Robert Lowry

1. Low   in the grave He lay— Je - sus my Sav-iour! Wait-ing the com-ing day—
2. Vain - ly they watch His bed—Je - sus my Sav-iour! Vain-ly they seal the dead—
3. Death cannot keep his prey—Je - sus my Sav-iour! He   tore the bars a - way—

REFRAIN *Faster*

Je - sus my   Lord!   Up from the grave He a - rose,   With a
                                He a-rose!

might - y tri-umph o'er His foes;   He a - rose a Vic-tor from the
                        He a-rose!

dark do - main, And He lives for - ev - er with His saints to reign, He a-

rit.

rose!   He a-rose!   Hal - le - lu - jah! Christ a - rose!
He   a-rose!   He   a-rose!

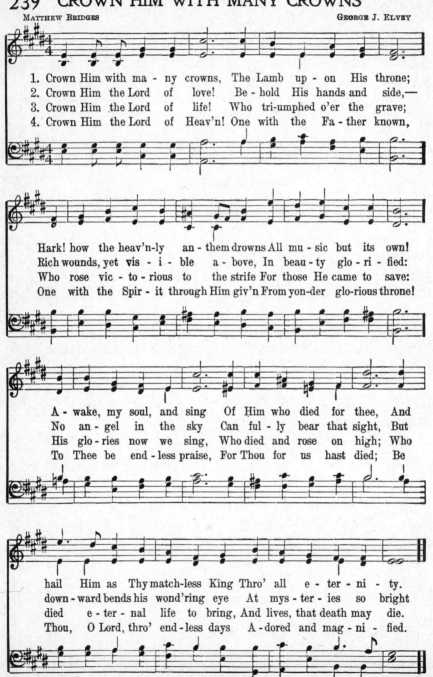

239 CROWN HIM WITH MANY CROWNS

MATTHEW BRIDGES

GEORGE J. ELVEY

1. Crown Him with ma - ny crowns, The Lamb up - on His throne;
2. Crown Him the Lord of love! Be - hold His hands and side,—
3. Crown Him the Lord of life! Who tri - umphed o'er the grave;
4. Crown Him the Lord of Heav'n! One with the Fa - ther known,

Hark! how the heav'n-ly an - them drowns All mu - sic but its own!
Rich wounds, yet vis - i - ble a - bove, In beau - ty glo - ri - fied:
Who rose vic - to - rious to the strife For those He came to save:
One with the Spir - it through Him giv'n From yon-der glo-rious throne!

A - wake, my soul, and sing Of Him who died for thee, And
No an - gel in the sky Can ful - ly bear that sight, But
His glo - ries now we sing, Who died and rose on high; Who
To Thee be end - less praise, For Thou for us hast died; Be

hail Him as Thy match-less King Thro' all e - ter - ni - ty.
down - ward bends his wond'ring eye At mys - ter - ies so bright
died e - ter - nal life to bring, And lives, that death may die.
Thou, O Lord, thro' end - less days A - dored and mag - ni - fied.

240 WE'RE MARCHING TO ZION

ISAAC WATTS

ROBERT LOWRY

Spirited

1. Come, we that love the Lord, And let our joys be known, Join
2. Let those re - fuse to sing Who nev - er knew our God; But
3. The hill of Zi - on yields A thou - sand sa - cred sweets Be -
4. Then let our songs abound, And ev - 'ry tear be dry; We're

in a song with sweet ac - cord, Join in a song with sweet accord, And
chil - dren of the heav'n-ly King, But chil - dren of the heav'nly King, May
fore we reach the heav'n-ly fields, Be-fore we reach the heav'nly fields, Or
marching thro' Immanuel's ground, We're marching thro' Immanuel's ground, To

thus sur - round the throne, And thus sur-round the throne.
speak their joys a - broad, May speak their joys a - broad.
walk the gold - en streets, Or walk the gold - en streets.
fair - er worlds on high, To fair - er worlds on high.

thus sur - round the throne, And thus sur - round the throne.

CHORUS

We're march - ing to Zi - on, Beau-ti - ful, beau-ti-ful Zi - on; We're
We're marching on to Zi - on,

march-ing upward to Zi - on, The beau - ti-ful cit - y of God.
Zi - on, Zi-on,

241 MOTHER'S PRAYERS HAVE FOLLOWED ME

Lizzie DeArmond.

B. D. Ackley

1. I grieved my Lord from day to day, I scorned His love so full and free, And though I wan-dered far a-way, My moth-er's pray'rs have fol-lowed me.

2. O'er des-ert wild, o'er mountain high A wan-der-er I chose to be, A wretch-ed soul con-demned to die, Still moth-er's pray'rs have fol-lowed me.

3. He turned my dark-ness in-to light, This bless-ed Christ of Cal-va-ry, I'll praise His name both day and night, That moth-er's pray'rs have fol-lowed me.

REFRAIN.

I'm com-ing home, I'm com-ing home, To live my wast-ed life a-new, For moth-er's pray'rs have fol-lowed me, Have fol-lowed me the whole world thro'.

242 MY MOTHER'S PRAYER

J. W. Van De Venter

W. S. Weeden
Arr.–A. T. Hardy

With feeling

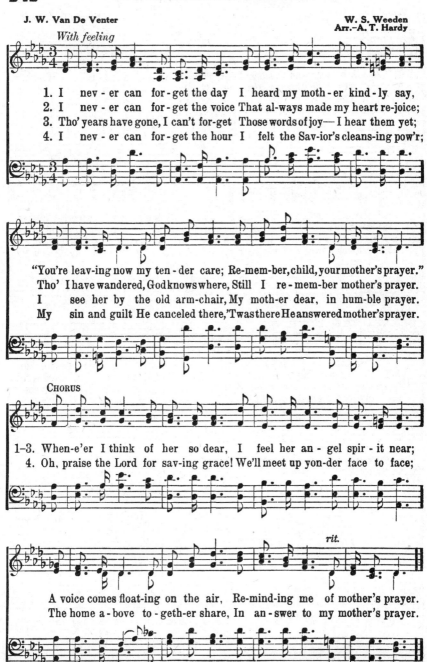

1. I nev-er can for-get the day I heard my moth-er kind-ly say,
2. I nev-er can for-get the voice That al-ways made my heart re-joice;
3. Tho' years have gone, I can't for-get Those words of joy—I hear them yet;
4. I nev-er can for-get the hour I felt the Sav-ior's cleans-ing pow'r;

"You're leav-ing now my ten-der care; Re-mem-ber, child, your mother's prayer."
Tho' I have wandered, God knows where, Still I re-mem-ber mother's prayer.
I see her by the old arm-chair, My moth-er dear, in hum-ble prayer.
My sin and guilt He canceled there, 'Twas there He answered mother's prayer.

CHORUS

1-3. When-e'er I think of her so dear, I feel her an-gel spir-it near;
4. Oh, praise the Lord for sav-ing grace! We'll meet up yon-der face to face;

rit.

A voice comes float-ing on the air, Re-mind-ing me of mother's prayer.
The home a-bove to-geth-er share, In an-swer to my mother's prayer.

243 MY MOTHER'S BIBLE

Evangelist M. B. Williams

Charlie D. Tillman

DUET

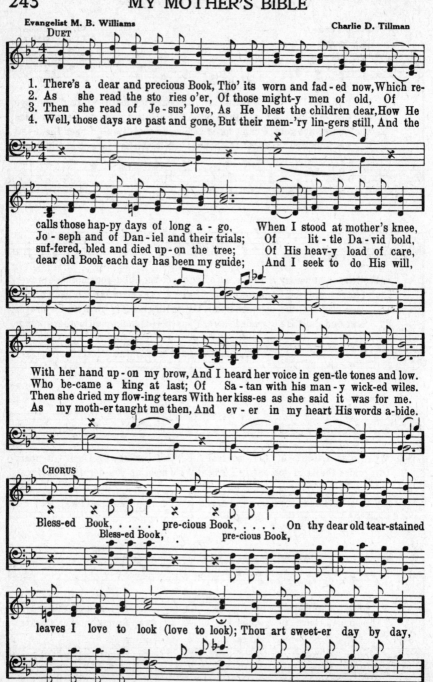

1. There's a dear and precious Book, Tho' its worn and fad-ed now, Which re-
2. As she read the sto-ries o'er, Of those might-y men of old, Of
3. Then she read of Je-sus' love, As He blest the children dear, How He
4. Well, those days are past and gone, But their mem-'ry lin-gers still, And the

calls those hap-py days of long a-go, When I stood at mother's knee,
Jo-seph and of Dan-iel and their trials; Of lit-tle Da-vid bold,
suf-fered, bled and died up-on the tree; Of His heav-y load of care,
dear old Book each day has been my guide; And I seek to do His will,

With her hand up-on my brow, And I heard her voice in gen-tle tones and low.
Who be-came a king at last; Of Sa-tan with his man-y wick-ed wiles.
Then she dried my flow-ing tears With her kiss-es as she said it was for me.
As my moth-er taught me then, And ev-er in my heart His words a-bide.

CHORUS

Bless-ed Book, ... pre-cious Book, ... On thy dear old tear-stained
Bless-ed Book, pre-cious Book,

leaves I love to look (love to look); Thou art sweet-er day by day,

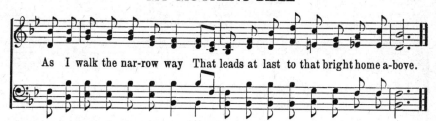

As I walk the nar-row way That leads at last to that bright home a-bove.

244 COME, YE FAITHFUL, RAISE THE STRAIN

John of Damascus
Tr. by John M. Neale

Arthur S. Sullivan

1. Come, ye faith-ful, raise the strain Of tri - um-phant gladness! God hath bro't His
2. 'Tis the spring of souls to - day: Christ hath burst His pris-on, From the frost and
3. Now the queen of seasons, bright With the day of splen-dor, With the roy - al
4. "Hal - le - lu - jah!" now we cry To our King Im - mor - tal, Who, triumphant,

Is - ra - el In - to joy from sad-ness, Loosed from Pharaoh's bitter yoke Jacob's
gloom of death Light and life have ris-en. All the win-ter of our sins, Long and
feast of feasts, Comes its joy to ren - der; Comes to glad Je - ru - sa - lem, Who, with
burst the bars Of the tomb's dark por-tal; "Hal - le - lu - jah!" with the Son, God the

sons and daughters, Led them with unmoistened foot Thru the Red Sea wa - ters.
dark, is fly - ing From His light to whom we give Thanks and praise un-dy-ing.
true af - fec - tion, Welcomes in un-wea-ried strains Je - sus' res - ur - rec - tion!
Fa-ther prais-ing; "Hal-le - lu - jah!" yet a - gain To the Spir - it rais-ing.

245 HIGHER GROUND

Johnson Oatman, Jr.   Chas. H. Gabriel

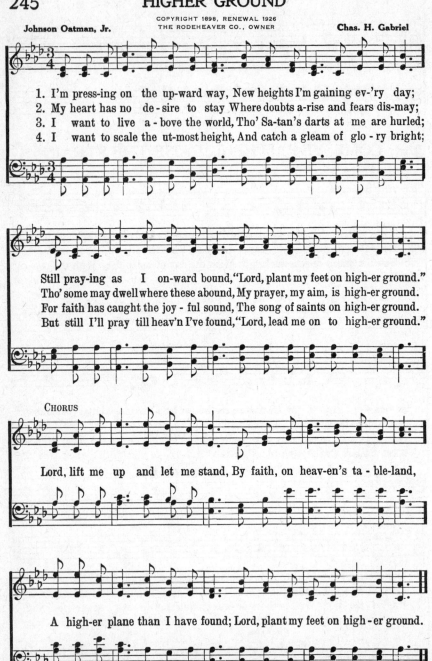

1. I'm press-ing on the up-ward way, New heights I'm gaining ev-'ry day;
2. My heart has no de-sire to stay Where doubts a-rise and fears dis-may;
3. I want to live a-bove the world, Tho' Sa-tan's darts at me are hurled;
4. I want to scale the ut-most height, And catch a gleam of glo-ry bright;

Still pray-ing as I on-ward bound, "Lord, plant my feet on high-er ground."
Tho' some may dwell where these abound, My prayer, my aim, is high-er ground.
For faith has caught the joy-ful sound, The song of saints on high-er ground.
But still I'll pray till heav'n I've found, "Lord, lead me on to high-er ground."

CHORUS

Lord, lift me up and let me stand, By faith, on heav-en's ta-ble-land,

A high-er plane than I have found; Lord, plant my feet on high-er ground.

246 SAVED TO THE UTTERMOST

"He is able also to save them to the uttermost that come unto God by Him."—HEB. 7 : 25

W. J. K.

W. J. KIRKPATRICK

1. Saved to the ut - ter-most: I am the Lord's Je - sus, my
2. Saved to the ut - ter-most: Je - sus is near; Keep - ing me
3. Saved to the ut - ter-most: this I can say, "Once all was
4. Saved to the ut - ter-most; cheer - ful - ly sing Loud hal - le -

Sav - ior, sal - va - tion af - fords; Gives me His Spir - it, a
safe - ly, He cast - eth out fear; Trust - ing His prom - is - es,
dark - ness, but now it is day; Beau - ti - ful vis - ions of
lu - ias to Je - sus, my King; Ran-somed and par - doned, re -

wit - ness with - in, Whisp'ring of par - don, and sav - ing from sin.
now I am blest; Lean - ing up - on Him, how sweet is my rest.
glo - ry I see, Je - sus in bright-ness re - vealed un - to me."
deemed by His blood, Cleansed from un - right-eous-ness; glo - ry to God!

REFRAIN

Saved, saved, saved to the ut - ter-most, Saved, saved by pow - er di - vine;

Saved, saved, saved to the ut - ter-most: Je - sus, the Sav-iour is mine!

247 HAVE YOU COUNTED THE COST?

A. J. H.

A. J. Hodge

1. There's a line that is drawn by re-ject-ing our Lord, Where the call of His
2. You may bar-ter your hope of e-ter-ni-ty's morn, For a mo-ment of
3. While the door of His mer-cy is o-pen to you, Ere the depth of His

Spir-it is lost,.... And you hur-ry along with the pleasure-mad throng—
joy at the most,.... For the glit-ter of sin and the things it will win—
love you ex-haust,... Won't you come and be healed, won't you whisper, I yield—

rit. *p*

CHORUS.

rit.

Have you counted, have you counted the cost?
Have you counted, have you counted the cost? Have you counted the cost, if your
I have counted, I have counted the cost.

pp

a tempo

soul should be lost, Tho' you gain the whole world for your own?..... E-ven

rit. *p*

now it may be that the line you have crossed, Have you counted, have you counted the cost?

248   IS YOUR ALL ON THE ALTAR?

E. A. Hoffman

Elisha A. Hoffman

1. You have longed for sweet peace, and for faith to increase, And have ear-nest-ly,
2. Would you walk with the Lord, in the light of His Word, And have peace and con-
3. Oh, we nev-er can know what the Lord will be-stow Of the bless-ings for
4. Who can tell all the love He will send from a-bove, And how hap-py our

fer-vent-ly prayed; But you can-not have rest, or be per-fect-ly blest
tent-ment al-way, You must do His sweet will, to be free from all ill,
which we have prayed, Till our bod-y and soul He doth ful-ly con-trol,
hearts will be made, Of the fel-low-ship sweet we shall share at His feet,

CHORUS

Un-til all on the al-tar is laid.
On the al-tar your all you must lay.   Is your all on the al-tar of
And our all on the al-tar is laid.
When our all on the al-tar is laid?

sac-ri-fice laid? Your heart, does the Spirit con-trol? . . . You can on-ly be

blest and have peace and sweet rest, As you yield Him your bod-y and soul.

249 I'LL LIVE FOR HIM

R. E. Hudson
C. R. Dunbar

1. My life, my love, I give to Thee, Thou Lamb of God who died for me;
2. I now be-lieve Thou dost re-ceive, For Thou hast died that I might live;
3. O Thou who died on Cal-va-ry, To save my soul and make me free,

CHO.—I'll live for Him who died for me, How hap-py then my life shall be!

D.C. Chorus

Oh, may I ev-er faith-ful be, My Sav-ior and my God!
And now hence-forth I'll trust in Thee, My Sav-ior and my God!
I'll con-se-crate my life to Thee, My Sav-ior and my God!

I'll live for Him who died for me, My Sav-ior and my God!

250 I SURRENDER ALL

J. W. Van Deventer
W. S. Weeden

1. All to Je-sus I sur-ren-der, All to Him I free-ly give;
2. All to Je-sus I sur-ren-der, Hum-bly at His feet I bow,
3. All to Je-sus I sur-ren-der, Make me, Sav-ior, whol-ly Thine;
4. All to Je-sus I sur-ren-der, Lord, I give my-self to Thee;
5. All to Je-sus I sur-ren-der, Now I feel the sa-cred flame;

I will ev-er love and trust Him, In His pres-ence dai-ly live.
World-ly pleas-ures all for-sak-en, Take me, Je-sus, take me now.
Let me feel the Ho-ly Spir-it,—Tru-ly know that Thou art mine.
Fill me with Thy love and pow-er, Let Thy bless-ing fall on me.
Oh, the joy of full sal-va-tion! Glo-ry, glo-ry to His name!

I SURRENDER ALL

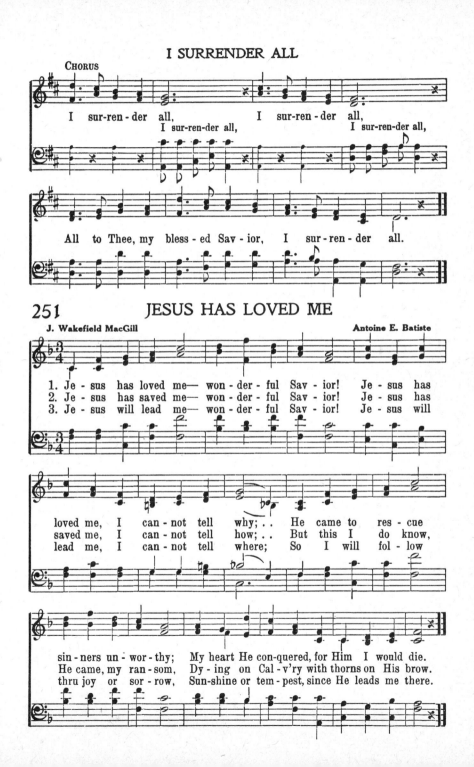

Chorus

I sur-ren-der all,   I sur-ren-der all,
I sur-ren-der all,   I sur-ren-der all,

All to Thee, my bless-ed Sav-ior, I sur-ren-der all.

251   JESUS HAS LOVED ME

J. Wakefield MacGill   Antoine E. Batiste

1. Je - sus has loved me— won - der - ful Sav - ior! Je - sus has
2. Je - sus has saved me— won - der - ful Sav - ior! Je - sus has
3. Je - sus will lead me— won - der - ful Sav - ior! Je - sus will

loved me, I can - not tell why; .. He came to res - cue
saved me, I can - not tell how; .. But this I do know,
lead me, I can - not tell where; So I will fol - low

sin - ners un - wor - thy; My heart He con-quered, for Him I would die.
He came, my ran - som, Dy - ing on Cal - v'ry with thorns on His brow.
thru joy or sor - row, Sun-shine or tem - pest, since He leads me there.

252 I'LL GO WHERE YOU WANT ME TO GO

MARY BROWN   CARRIE E. ROUNSEFELL

1. It may not be on the mountain height, Or o - ver the storm - y sea,
2. Perhaps to - day there are lov - ing words Which Jesus would have me speak;
3. There's surely somewhere a low - ly place In earth's harvest fields so wide,

It may not be at the bat - tle's front My Lord will have need of me;
There may be now in the paths of sin Some wand'rer whom I should seek:
Where I may la - bor thro' life's short day For Je - sus, the Cru - ci - fied;

But if, by a still, small voice He calls To paths that I do not know,
O Sav - ior, if Thou wilt be my guide, Tho' dark and rug-ged the way,
So trust-ing my all to Thy ten-der care, And knowing Thou lov - est me,

I'll answer, dear Lord, with my hand in Thine, I'll go where you want me to go.
My voice shall ech - o the mes-sage sweet, I'll say what you want me to say.
I'll do Thy will with a heart sin-cere, I'll be what you want me to be.

REFRAIN

I'll go where you want me to go, dear Lord, Over mountain, or plain, or sea;

I'LL GO WHERE YOU WANT ME TO GO

I'll say what you want me to say, dear Lord, I'll be what you want me to be.

253 TRANSFORMED

Mrs. F. G. Burroughs   B. D. Ackley

1. Dear Lord, take up my tan-gled strands, Where we have wrought in vain,
2. Touch Thou the sad, dis-cord-ant keys Of ev-'ry troub-led breast,
3. Where bro-ken vows in frag-ments lie— The toll of wast-ed years,—
4. Take all the fail-ures, each mis-take Of our poor, hu-man ways,

That by the skill of Thy dear hands Some beau-ty may re-main.
And change to peace-ful har-mo-nies The sigh-ings of un-rest.
Do Thou make whole a-gain, we cry, And give a song for tears.
Then, Sav-ior, for Thine own dear sake, Make them show forth Thy praise.

CHORUS

Transformed by grace di-vine, The glo-ry shall be Thine;
Trans-formed   The glo-ry

To Thy most ho-ly will, O Lord, We now our all re-sign.

254   O JESUS, I HAVE PROMISED

JOHN E. BODE

ARTHUR H. MANN

1. O Je-sus, I have promised To serve Thee to the end; Be Thou for-ev - er
2. O let me feel Thee near me, The world is ev - er near; I see the sights that
3. O Jesus, Thou hast promised To all who fol-low Thee That where Thou art in

near me, My Mas-ter and my Friend: I shall not fear the bat - tle If Thou art
dazzle, The tempting sounds I hear: My foes are ev - er near me, Around me
glo - ry There shall Thy servant be; And, Je - sus, I have promised To serve Thee

by my side, Nor wan-der from the path - way If Thou wilt be my Guide.
and with - in; But, Je - sus, draw Thou nearer, And shield my soul from sin.
to the end; O give me grace to fol - low My Mas - ter and my Friend.

255   TAKE MY LIFE, AND LET IT BE

Frances R. Havergal

C. H. A. Malan

1. Take my life, and let it be Con-se - cra - ted, Lord, to Thee; Take my hands, and
2. Take my feet, and let them be Swift and beau-ti - ful for Thee; Take my voice, and
3. Take my sil - ver and my gold, Not a mite would I with-hold; Take my mo-ments
4. Take my will and make it Thine, It shall be no lon-ger mine; Take my heart, it

TAKE MY LIFE, AND LET IT BE

let them move At the im-pulse of Thy love, At the im-pulse of Thy love.
let me sing Al-ways, on-ly, for my King, Al-ways, on-ly, for my King.
and my days, Let them flow in cease-less praise, Let them flow in ceaseless praise.
is Thine own, It shall be Thy roy-al throne, It shall be Thy roy-al throne.

256 HAVE THINE OWN WAY, LORD

A. A. P.

GEO. C. STEBBINS

Slowly

1. Have Thine own way, Lord! Have Thine own way! Thou art the
2. Have Thine own way, Lord! Have Thine own way! Search me and
3. Have Thine own way, Lord! Have Thine own way! Wound-ed and
4. Have Thine own way, Lord! Have Thine own way! Hold o'er my

Pot - ter; I am the clay Mould me and make me Aft - er Thy
try me, Mas-ter, to - day! Whit - er than snow, Lord, Wash me just
wea - ry, Help me, I pray! Pow - er—all pow - er—Sure-ly is
be - ing Ab - so - lute sway! Fill with Thy Spir - it Till all shall

will, While I am wait - ing, Yield - ed and still.
now, As in Thy pres - ence Hum - bly I bow.
Thine! Touch me and heal me, Sav - ior di - vine!
see Christ on - ly, al - ways, Liv - ing in me!

JESUS, BLESSED JESUS

Chas. H. Gabriel

Chas. H. Gabriel

Very effective as a Duet.

1. There's One who can com-fort when all else fails, Je - sus, bless-ed Je - sus;
2. He hear-eth the cry of the soul dis-tressed, Je - sus, bless-ed Je - sus;
3. He nev - er for-sakes in the dark-est hour, Je - sus, bless-ed Je - sus;
4. What joy it will be when we see His face, Je - sus, bless-ed Je - sus;

A Sav - ior who saves tho' the foe as - sails, Je - sus, bless-ed Je - sus:
He heal-eth the wound-ed, He giv - eth rest, Je - sus, bless-ed Je - sus:
His arm is a - round us with keep-ing pow'r, Je - sus, bless-ed Je - sus:
For - ev - er to sing of His love and grace, Je - sus, bless-ed Je - sus:

Once He trav - eled the way we go, Felt the pangs of de - ceit and woe;
When from loved ones we're called to part, When the tears in our an-guish start,
When we en - ter the Shad-ow - land, When at Jor - dan we trem-bling stand,
There at home on that shin-ing shore, With the loved ones gone on be - fore,

Who more per - fect-ly then can know Than Je - sus, bless-ed Je - sus?
None can com - fort the break-ing heart Like Je - sus, bless-ed Je - sus.
He will meet us with outstretched hand, This Je - sus, bless-ed Je - sus.
We will praise Him for - ev - er - more, Our Je - sus, bless-ed Je - sus.

258 JUST AS I AM, THINE OWN TO BE

Marianne Hearn

Joseph Barnby

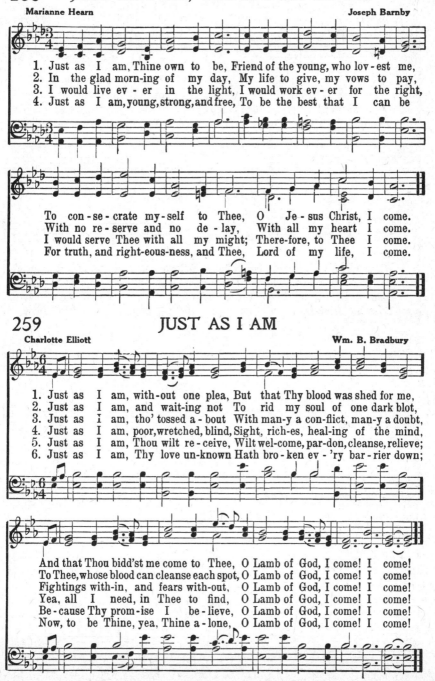

1. Just as I am, Thine own to be, Friend of the young, who lov-est me,
2. In the glad morn-ing of my day, My life to give, my vows to pay,
3. I would live ev - er in the light, I would work ev - er for the right,
4. Just as I am, young, strong, and free, To be the best that I can be

To con-se-crate my-self to Thee, O Je - sus Christ, I come.
With no re - serve and no de - lay, With all my heart I come.
I would serve Thee with all my might; There-fore, to Thee I come.
For truth, and right-eous-ness, and Thee, Lord of my life, I come.

259 JUST AS I AM

Charlotte Elliott

Wm. B. Bradbury

1. Just as I am, with-out one plea, But that Thy blood was shed for me,
2. Just as I am, and wait-ing not To rid my soul of one dark blot,
3. Just as I am, tho' tossed a - bout With man-y a con-flict, man-y a doubt,
4. Just as I am, poor, wretched, blind, Sight, rich-es, heal-ing of the mind,
5. Just as I am, Thou wilt re - ceive, Wilt wel-come, par-don, cleanse, relieve;
6. Just as I am, Thy love un-known Hath bro - ken ev - 'ry bar-rier down;

And that Thou bidd'st me come to Thee, O Lamb of God, I come! I come!
To Thee, whose blood can cleanse each spot, O Lamb of God, I come! I come!
Fightings with-in, and fears with-out, O Lamb of God, I come! I come!
Yea, all I need, in Thee to find, O Lamb of God, I come! I come!
Be-cause Thy prom-ise I be-lieve, O Lamb of God, I come! I come!
Now, to be Thine, yea, Thine a-lone, O Lamb of God, I come! I come!

260 WHY NOT NOW?

EL NATHAN

C. C. CASE

1. While we pray and while we plead, While you see your soul's deep need,
2. You have wandered far a - way; Do not risk an - oth - er day;
3. In the world you've failed to find Aught of peace for troub - led mind;
4. Come to Christ, con - fes - sion make; Come to Christ, and par - don take;

While our Fa - ther calls you home, Will you not, my broth - er, come?
Do not turn from God thy face, But to - day ac - cept His grace.
Come to Christ, on Him be - lieve, Peace and joy you shall re - ceive.
Trust in Him from day to day, He will keep you all the way.

CHORUS

Why not now? ... Why not now? ... Why not come to Je - sus now?
Why not now?   Why not now?

Why not now? ... Why not now? ... Why not come to Je - sus now?
Why not now?   Why not now?

261 I AM COMING HOME

A. H. ACKLEY

B. D. ACKLEY

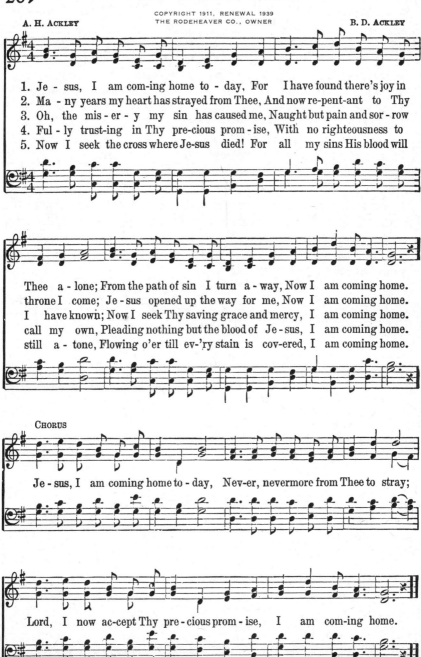

1. Je - sus, I am com-ing home to - day, For   I have found there's joy in
2. Ma - ny years my heart has strayed from Thee, And now re-pent-ant   to Thy
3. Oh, the mis - er - y my sin has caused me, Naught but pain and sor - row
4. Ful - ly trust-ing in Thy pre-cious prom - ise, With no righteousness to
5. Now I seek the cross where Je-sus died! For all   my sins His blood will

Thee a - lone; From the path of sin I turn a - way, Now I am coming home.
throne I come; Je - sus opened up the way for me, Now I am coming home.
I have known; Now I seek Thy saving grace and mercy, I am coming home.
call my own, Pleading nothing but the blood of Je - sus, I am coming home.
still a - tone, Flowing o'er till ev-'ry stain is cov-ered, I am coming home.

CHORUS

Je - sus, I am coming home to - day, Nev - er, nevermore from Thee to stray;

Lord, I now ac-cept Thy pre - cious prom - ise, I   am com-ing home.

262 REVIVE US AGAIN

Wm. P. Mackay

John J. Husband

1. We praise Thee, O God! for the Son of Thy love, For Je-sus who
2. We praise Thee, O God! for Thy Spir-it of light, Who has shown us our
3. All glo-ry and praise to the Lamb that was slain, Who has borne all our
4. Re-vive us a-gain; fill each heart with Thy love; May each soul be re-

Chorus

died, and is now gone a-bove.
Sav-ior, and scat-tered our night. Hal-le-lu-jah! Thine the glo-ry, Hal-le-
sins, and has cleansed ev-'ry stain.
kin-dled with fire from a-bove.

lu-jah! A-men; Hal-le-lu-jah! Thine the glo-ry, re-vive us a-gain.

263 THE GREAT PHYSICIAN

Wm. Hunter

J. H. Stockton

1. The great Phy-si-cian now is near, The sym-pa-thiz-ing Je-sus;
2. Your man-y sins are all for-giv'n, O hear the voice of Je-sus;
3. All glo-ry to the dy-ing Lamb, I now be-lieve in Je-sus;
4. His name dis-pels my guilt and fear, No oth-er name but Je-sus;

THE GREAT PHYSICIAN

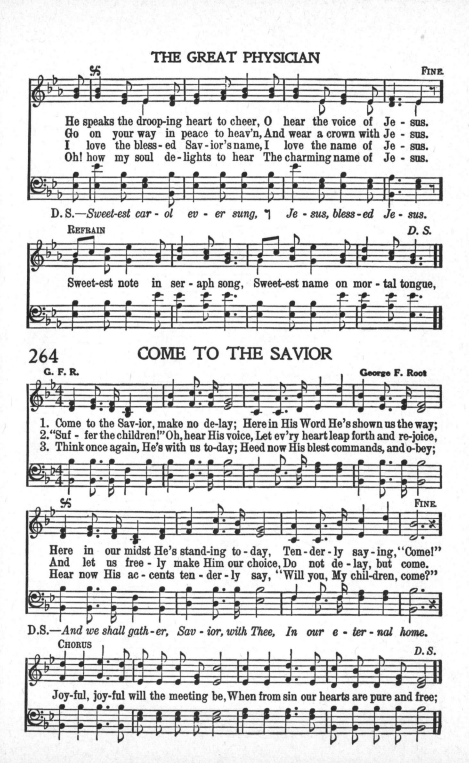

He speaks the droop-ing heart to cheer, O hear the voice of Je - sus.
Go on your way in peace to heav'n, And wear a crown with Je - sus.
I love the bless - ed Sav - ior's name, I love the name of Je - sus.
Oh! how my soul de - lights to hear The charming name of Je - sus.

D. S.—*Sweet-est car - ol ev - er sung, Je - sus, bless-ed Je - sus.*

REFRAIN

Sweet-est note in ser - aph song, Sweet-est name on mor - tal tongue,

264 COME TO THE SAVIOR

G. F. R.   George F. Root

1. Come to the Sav-ior, make no de-lay; Here in His Word He's shown us the way;
2. "Suf - fer the children!" Oh, hear His voice, Let ev'ry heart leap forth and re-joice,
3. Think once again, He's with us to-day; Heed now His blest commands, and o-bey;

Here in our midst He's stand-ing to - day, Ten - der - ly say - ing, "Come!"
And let us free - ly make Him our choice, Do not de - lay, but come.
Hear now His ac - cents ten - der - ly say, "Will you, My chil-dren, come?"

D.S.—*And we shall gath - er, Sav - ior, with Thee, In our e - ter - nal home.*

CHORUS

Joy-ful, joy-ful will the meeting be, When from sin our hearts are pure and free;

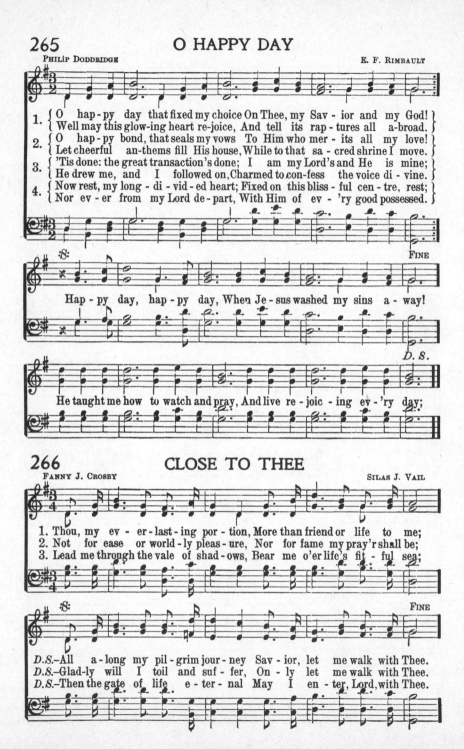

265

O HAPPY DAY

PHILIP DODDRIDGE

E. F. RIMBAULT

1. O hap-py day that fixed my choice On Thee, my Sav-ior and my God!
Well may this glow-ing heart re-joice, And tell its rap-tures all a-broad.

2. O hap-py bond, that seals my vows To Him who mer-its all my love!
Let cheerful an-thems fill His house, While to that sa-cred shrine I move.

3. 'Tis done: the great transaction's done; I am my Lord's and He is mine;
He drew me, and I followed on, Charmed to con-fess the voice di-vine.

4. Now rest, my long-di-vid-ed heart; Fixed on this bliss-ful cen-tre, rest;
Nor ev-er from my Lord de-part, With Him of ev-'ry good possessed.

FINE

Hap-py day, hap-py day, When Je-sus washed my sins a-way!

D. S.

He taught me how to watch and pray, And live re-joic-ing ev-'ry day;

266

CLOSE TO THEE

FANNY J. CROSBY

SILAS J. VAIL

1. Thou, my ev-er-last-ing por-tion, More than friend or life to me;
2. Not for ease or world-ly pleas-ure, Nor for fame my pray'r shall be;
3. Lead me through the vale of shad-ows, Bear me o'er life's fit-ful sea;

FINE

D.S.—All a-long my pil-grim jour-ney Sav-ior, let me walk with Thee.
D.S.—Glad-ly will I toil and suf-fer, On-ly let me walk with Thee.
D.S.—Then the gate of life e-ter-nal May I en-ter, Lord, with Thee.

CLOSE TO THEE

D. S.

REFRAIN

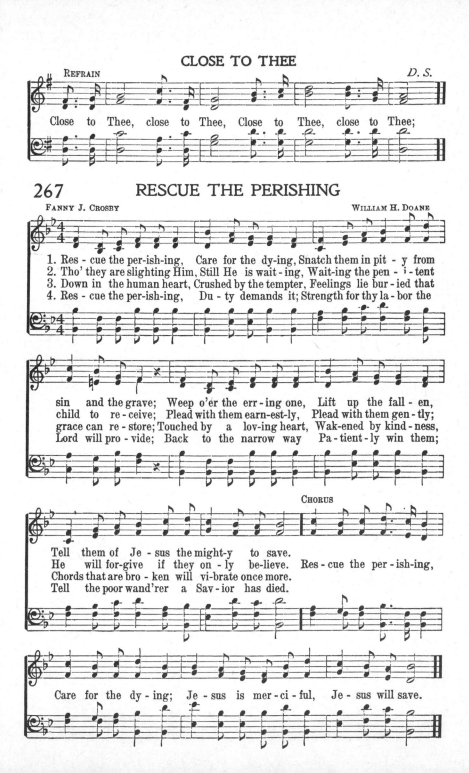

Close to Thee, close to Thee, Close to Thee, close to Thee;

267   RESCUE THE PERISHING

FANNY J. CROSBY

WILLIAM H. DOANE

1. Res - cue the per-ish-ing, Care for the dy-ing, Snatch them in pit - y from
2. Tho' they are slighting Him, Still He is wait-ing, Wait-ing the pen - i - tent
3. Down in the human heart, Crushed by the tempter, Feelings lie bur-ied that
4. Res - cue the per-ish-ing, Du - ty demands it; Strength for thy la - bor the

sin and the grave; Weep o'er the err-ing one, Lift up the fall - en,
child to re - ceive; Plead with them earn-est-ly, Plead with them gen - tly;
grace can re - store; Touched by a lov-ing heart, Wak-ened by kind - ness,
Lord will pro - vide; Back to the narrow way Pa - tient - ly win them;

CHORUS

Tell them of Je - sus the might-y to save.
He will for-give if they on - ly be-lieve. Res - cue the per - ish-ing,
Chords that are bro - ken will vi-brate once more.
Tell the poor wand'rer a Sav - ior has died.

Care for the dy - ing; Je - sus is mer - ci - ful, Je - sus will save.

268 HE BROUGHT ME OUT

Rev. H. J. Zelley
Cho. by H. L. G.

H. L. Gilmour

1. My heart was dis-tressed 'neath Je-ho-vah's dread frown, And low in the
2. He placed me up - on the strong Rock by His side, My steps were es-
3. He gave me a song, 'twas a new song of praise, By day and by
4. I'll sing of His won-der-ful mer-cy to me, I'll praise Him till

pit where my sins dragged me down; I cried to the Lord from the
tab-lished and here I'll a - bide; No dan-ger of fall - ing while
night its sweet notes I will raise; My heart's o - ver-flow-ing, I'm
all men His good-ness shall see; I'll sing of sal - va-tion at

deep mir - y clay, Who ten - der-ly brought me out to gold - en day.
here I re-main, But stand by His grace un-til the crown I gain.
hap - py and free, I'll praise my Re - deem-er, who has res - cued me.
home and a - broad, Till man - y shall hear the truth and trust in God.

CHORUS

He brought me out of the mir - y clay, He set my feet on the Rock to stay;

He puts a song in my soul to - day, A song of praise, hal-le - lu - jah!

AT THE CROSS

Isaac Watts

R. E. Hudson

1. A - las! and did my Sav - ior bleed? And did my Sov'reign die?
2. Was it for crimes that I had done, He groaned up-on the tree?
3. Well might the sun in dark-ness hide, And shut his glo - ries in,
4. But drops of grief can ne'er re - pay The debt of love I owe:

Would He de - vote that sa - cred head For such a worm as I?
A - maz - ing pit - y! grace unknown! And love be - yond de - gree!
When Christ, the mighty Mak - er, died For man the crea-ture's sin.
Here, Lord, I give my - self a - way,—'Tis all that I can do.

CHORUS

At the cross, at the cross where I first saw the light, And the

bur-den of my heart rolled a - way, rolled a - way, It was there by

faith I received my sight, And now I am hap - py all the day.

270 ALMOST PERSUADED

P. P. B.   P. P. Bliss

1. "Al - most per-suad - ed," now to be - lieve; "Al - most per-suad - ed,"
2. "Al - most per-suad - ed," come, come to - day; "Al - most per-suad - ed,"
3. "Al - most per-suad - ed," har - vest is past! "Al - most per-suad - ed,"

Christ to re - ceive; Seems now some soul to say, "Go, Spir - it,
turn not a - way; Je - sus in - vites you here, An - gels are
doom comes at last! "Al - most" can - not a - vail; "Al - most" is

go Thy way, Some more con - ven - ient day On Thee I'll call."
lin - g'ring near, Prayers rise from hearts so dear, O wan-d'rer, come.
but to fail! Sad, sad, that bit - ter wail, "Al - most," but lost!

271 ONLY TRUST HIM

J. H. S.   J. H. Stockton

1. Come, ev - 'ry soul by sin op-pressed, There's mer-cy with the Lord,
2. For Je - sus shed His pre - cious blood, Rich bless-ings to be - stow;
3. Yes, Je - sus is the Truth, the Way, That leads you in - to rest:

And He will sure - ly give you rest By trust-ing in His Word.
Plunge now in - to the crim - son flood That wash-es white as snow.
Be - lieve in Him with-out de - lay, And you are ful - ly blest.

ONLY TRUST HIM

REFRAIN

Only trust Him, only trust Him, Only trust Him now;
He will save you, He will save you, He will (*Omit . . .*) save you now.

272   OH, WHY NOT TO-NIGHT?

J. Calvin Bushey

1. Oh, do not let the world de-part, And close thine eyes against the light;
2. To-mor-row's sun may nev-er rise To bless thy long de-lud-ed sight;
3. Our Lord in pit-y lin-gers still, And wilt thou thus His love re-quite?
4. Our bless-ed Lord re-fus-es none Who would to Him their souls u-nite;

Poor sin-ner, hard-en not your heart, Be saved, oh, to-night.
This is the time, oh, then, be wise, Be saved, oh, to-night.
Re-nounce at once thy stub-born will, Be saved, oh, to-night.
Be-lieve, o-bey, the work is done, Be saved, oh, to-night.

CHORUS

Oh, why not to-night? Oh, why not to-night?
Oh, why not to-night? why not to-night? Why not to-night? why not to-night?

Wilt thou be saved? Then why not to-night?
Wilt thou be saved? wilt thou be saved? Then why not, oh, why not to-night?

273 HE IS KNOCKING

E. E. HEWITT

B. D. ACKLEY

1. He is knock-ing, soft-ly knock-ing at the door; Let Him in, ...
2. He is call-ing, gen-tly call-ing to you now; Let Him in, ...
3. He is wait-ing, kind-ly wait-ing still for you; Let Him in, ...

O let Him in,

O let Him in; He will bring you rich-est bless-ing ev-er-more;
O let Him in; See the plead-ing dews of mer-cy on His brow;
O let Him in; Give Him welcome, joy-ful welcome, warm and true;

O let Him in;

CHORUS

Let Him in, ... O let Him in! Knock-ing! knock-ing!
O let Him in, O let Him in!

O-pen wide the door, Let Him in to-day, Ask Him in to stay;
O let Him in, Ask Him in, He's

Knock-ing, knock-ing! life He will restore, When you o-pen wide the door.
bolt-ed door.

SOFTLY AND TENDERLY

W. L. T.   WILL L. THOMPSON

Very slow pp

1. Soft - ly and ten-der - ly Je - sus is call-ing, Call - ing for you and for me;
2. Why should we tarry when Jesus is plead-ing, Pleading for you and for me?
3. Time is now fleeting, the moments are passing, Passing from you and from me;
4. Oh! for the won-der-ful love He has promised, Promised for you and for me;

See, on the portals He's waiting and watching, Watching for you and for me.
Why should we linger and heed not His mercies, Mer-cies for you and for me?
Shadows are gathering, death-beds are coming, Com-ing for you and for me.
Tho' we have sinned, He has mercy and pardon, Par-don for you and for me.

CHORUS m   cresc.

Come home,.. come home,...... Ye who are wear-y, come home;...
Come home,   come home,

pp   ppp   rit.   pp

Ear-nest-ly, ten-der-ly, Je - sus is call-ing, Call-ing, O sin-ner, come home!

275 ARE YOU COMING HOME TONIGHT?

S. M. J.

James McGranahan

1. Are you com-ing Home, ye wand'rers, Whom Je-sus died to win,
2. Are you com-ing Home, ye lost ones? Be-hold your Lord doth wait:
3. Are you com-ing Home, ye guilt-y, Who bear the load of sin?
4. Are you com-ing Home, ye wea-ry, Who long for rest and peace?

All foot-sore, lame and wea-ry, Your gar-ments stained with sin?
Come, then, no lon-ger lin-ger, Come ere it be too late;
Out-side you've long been stand-ing, Come now and ven-ture in;
Your bur-den has been heav-y, And long you've sought re-lease;

Will you seek the blood of Je-sus, To wash your gar-ments white?
Will you come and let Him save you? Oh! trust His love and might;
Will you heed the Sav-ior's prom-ise, And dare to trust Him quite?
Will you now ac-cept of Je-sus, In Him your heart de-light?

Will you trust His pre-cious prom-ise, Are you com-ing Home to-night?
Will you come while He is call-ing, Are you com-ing Home to-night?
"Come un-to Me," saith Je-sus; Are you com-ing Home to-night?
Will you ful-ly yield up to Him, Are you com-ing Home to-night?

CHORUS

Are you com-ing Home to-night? Are you com-ing Home to-night?

ARE YOU COMING HOME TONIGHT?

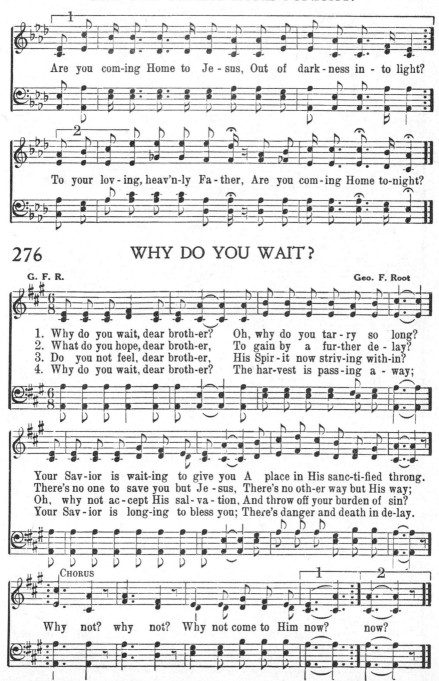

Are you com-ing Home to Je - sus, Out of dark - ness in - to light?

To your lov - ing, heav'n-ly Fa - ther, Are you com-ing Home to-night?

276   WHY DO YOU WAIT?

G. F. R.

Geo. F. Root

1. Why do you wait, dear broth-er?   Oh, why do you tar - ry so long?
2. What do you hope, dear broth-er,   To gain by a fur-ther de - lay?
3. Do you not feel, dear broth-er,   His Spir - it now striv-ing with-in?
4. Why do you wait, dear broth-er?   The har-vest is pass-ing a - way;

Your Sav-ior is wait-ing to give you A place in His sanc-ti-fied throng.
There's no one to save you but Je - sus, There's no oth-er way but His way;
Oh, why not ac-cept His sal - va-tion, And throw off your burden of sin?
Your Sav-ior is long-ing to bless you; There's danger and death in de-lay.

CHORUS

Why not? why not? Why not come to Him now?   now?

277 AWAKENING CHORUS

COPYRIGHT 1905, RENEWAL 1933
THE RODEHEAVER CO., OWNER

Charlotte G. Homer

Chas. H. Gabriel

1. A - wake! A-wake! a - wake! a-wake! and sing the bless - ed sto - ry; A-wake! A-wake! a-wake! a - wake! and let your song of praise a - rise; A-wake! a-wake! the earth is full of glo - ry, And light is beam - ing from the ra-diant skies; The rocks and rills, the vales and hills re-sound with glad-ness, All na - ture joins to sing the tri-umph

2. Ring out! Ring out! ring out! ring out! O bells of joy and glad - ness! Re-peat, Re-peat, re-peat re-peat a - new the sto - ry o'er a - gain, Till all the earth shall lose its weight of sad-ness, And shout a-new a-new the glo - ri-ous re - frain; With an - gels in the heights sing of the great sal - va - tion He wrest - ed from the hand of sin and

Male voices in Unison

AWAKENING CHORUS

THOU MIGHTY TO SAVE

Fanny J. Crosby

Chas. H. Gabriel

THOU MIGHTY TO SAVE

bright-er coun-try, A home with the pure and blest. . . .
Lord and Sav-ior, I'm trust-ing a - lone in Thee. . . .
strife is end-ed, I rest at Thy feet at last. . . .

CHORUS

And oh, when my course is fin - ished, And vic - tor's palm I
And oh, when my course is fin-ished, And vic - tor's

wave, ... To Thee will I give the glo - ry, . . . O
palm I wave, glo - ry, O

cres.

Thou, who art might - y to save, ... To Thee will I give the
save, To Thee

ff *slower*

glo - ry . . . . O Thou, who art might - y to save. . . .

279   MY ANCHOR HOLDS

(To my friends of the great Cadle Choir, Indianapolis)

Frank C. Huston   Frank C. Huston

With a positive joy

1. We all are fel-low sail-ors, Up-on the sea of life; For some, the
2. Tho' an-gry winds be blow-ing, And wild the storm-y sea, I'm safe with-
3. O friend, up-on life's o-cean, Where stormy bil-lows roll, There's One who

ship rides brave-ly, For some,'tis storm and strife. But I have found a ha-ven,
in the har-bor, No harm can come to me. With Je-sus as my ref-uge,
died to save you, He's long-ing for your soul. In Him I've found a shel-ter,

Where love my bark en-folds, And tho' fierce winds be blowing—My an-chor holds.
His love my soul en-folds, And what-so-e'er be-fall me, —My an-chor holds.
He peace and joy un-folds; Praise God! in such a ref-uge— My an-chor holds.

CHORUS

My an-chor holds, My an-chor holds! In Je-sus there is ref-uge, His

love en-folds. My an-chor holds, My an-chor holds, Tho'

MY ANCHOR HOLDS

Verses 1 & 2 ... D. C. ... **Verse 3** f ... ff

fierce the storms a-round me, My anchor holds. My an-chor holds . . .
(3) a-[*Omit* . . . . .]-round me, My an-chor holds, my an-chor

f dim. e rall. p — — — pp — — — p cres. f ff

holds, my an-chor holds, my an-chor holds, my an-chor holds. My an-chor holds.

280   WALKING CLOSE TO HIS SIDE

A. H. A.   Rev. A. H. Ackley

1. Walk-ing close to the Sav-ior, There is fel-low-ship sweet, Rest be-side the still
2. Walk-ing close to the Sav-ior, When temptations ap-pear, Just to know He is
3. Walk-ing close to the Sav-ior Gives me courage to bear Ev-'ry test that life
4. Walk-ing close to the Sav-ior, In the realm of the sky, Mid the glo-ries su-

REFRAIN

wa - ters, Pas-tures green for my feet.
with me Fills my heart with good cheer. Walk-ing close to His side, All my
brings me, Trou-ble, sor - row and care.
per - nal, I shall walk bye and bye.

need is sup-plied, He will keep me for-ev-er, While walking close to His side.

281 ALL HAIL, IMMANUEL!

D. R. van Sickle

Chas. H. Gabriel

1. All hail to Thee, Im-man-u-el, We cast . . . our crowns be-fore Thee;
2. All hail to Thee, Im-man-u-el, The ran - somed hosts surround Thee;
3. All hail to Thee, Im-man-u-el, Our ris - - en King and Sav-ior!

Let ev-'ry heart o-bey Thy will, And ev - - - 'ry voice a-
And earth-ly mon-archs clam-or forth Their Sov - - 'reign King to
Thy foes are van-quished, and Thou art Om-nip - - - o-tent for-

dore Thee. In praise to Thee, our Sav-ior King, The vi-brant
crown Thee. While those re-deemed in a-ges gone, As-sem-bled
ev-er. Death, sin and hell no lon-ger reign, And Sa-tan's

chords of Heav-en ring, And ech-o back the might-y strain:
round the great white throne, Break forth in-to im-mor-tal song:
pow'r is burst in twain; E-ter-nal glo-ry to Thy Name:

All hail! all hail! All hail! all hail! Im-man-u-el!
All hail! all hail!

ALL HAIL, IMMANUEL!

282 ALL HAIL THE POWER OF JESUS' NAME

E. Perronet   (DIADEM. C. M.)   James Eller

1. All hail the pow'r of Je - sus' name! Let an-gels pros-trate fall,
2. Ye cho - sen seed of Is - rael's race, Ye ran-somed from the fall,
3. Let ev - 'ry kin - dred, ev - 'ry tribe, On this ter - res-trial ball,
4. O that with yon - der sa - cred throng We at His feet may fall,

Let an - gels pros-trate fall; Bring forth the roy - al di - a - dem,
Ye ran-somed from the fall, Hail Him who saves you by His grace,
On this ter - res-trial ball, To Him all maj - es - ty as - cribe,
We at His feet may fall! We'll join the ev - er - last-ing song,

And crown............................ Him, Crown Him,

And crown Him, crown Him, crown Him, crown Him, And crown Him Lord of
And crown.. Him, Crown Him,

And crown Him, crown Him, crown Him, Crown...........................

crown Him, crown Him;

all, crown Him; And crown Him Lord of all! A - MEN.
crown......... Him;

.... Him; And crown Him Lord of all!

283 SAIL ON!

C. H. G.

Chas. H Gabriel.

Solo and chorus.

1. Up - on a wide and stormy sea, Thou'rt sail-ing to e - ter - ni - ty,
2. Art far from shore, and wea-ry-worn—The sky o'er-cast, the can-vas torn?
3. Do comrades trem - ble and re - fuse To fur - ther dare the taunting hues?
4. Do snarling waves thy craft as - sail? Art pow'rless, drift-ing with the gale?

Ad lib.

And thy great Ad-m'ral or-ders Thee:—"Sail on! sail on! sail on!"
Hark ye! a voice to thee is borne:—"Sail on! sail on! sail on!"
No oth - er course is thine to choose, Sail on! sail on! sail on!
Take heart! God's word shall nev - er fail! Sail on! sail on! sail on!

CHORUS.

Sail on! sail on! the storms will soon be past, The dark - ness
will not al - ways last; Sail on! sail on! sail on! God
Sail on! sail on! sail on!
lives! and He commands: "Sail on! sail on!"
on! sail on! sail on sail on!

Rit. e dim

pp

* May close here.

284 JESUS SHALL REIGN

Isaac Watts
Chorus Adapted

Haldor Lillenas

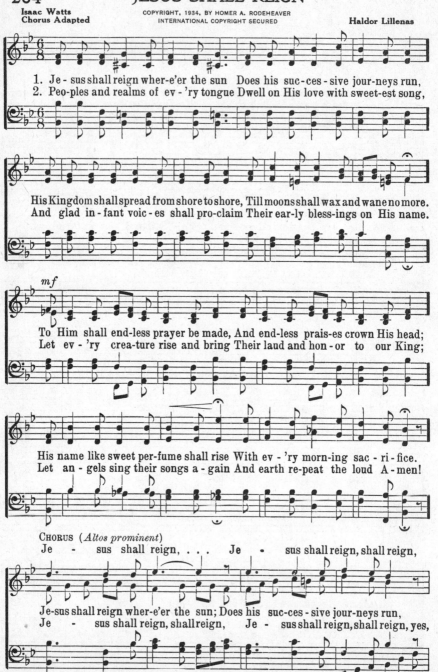

1. Je - sus shall reign wher-e'er the sun Does his suc-ces-sive jour-neys run,
2. Peo-ples and realms of ev - 'ry tongue Dwell on His love with sweet-est song,

His Kingdom shall spread from shore to shore, Till moons shall wax and wane no more.
And glad in - fant voic - es shall pro-claim Their ear-ly bless-ings on His name.

mf

To Him shall end-less prayer be made, And end-less prais-es crown His head;
Let ev - 'ry crea-ture rise and bring Their laud and hon - or to our King;

His name like sweet per-fume shall rise With ev - 'ry morn-ing sac - ri - fice.
Let an - gels sing their songs a - gain And earth re-peat the loud A - men!

CHORUS (*Altos prominent*)

Je - sus shall reign, . . . Je - sus shall reign, shall reign,

Je-sus shall reign wher-e'er the sun; Does his suc-ces - sive jour-neys run,
Je - sus shall reign, shall reign, Je - sus shall reign, shall reign, yes,

JESUS SHALL REIGN

Reign in re - gal maj - es - ty; End - less shall His king-dom be, And

bound - less His do - main, His vast do - main. . . . To
boundless and shoreless His vast do - main, His vast do - main. . . . To

bound - less and shoreless His vast domain, His vast domain, sing His praises! To

Him shall endless prayer be made, And end-less prais-es crown His head.

He is

Sopranos prominent

King of Kings and Lord of Lords, King of Kings and Lord of Lords,—

mf cres - - - - cen - - - - do   *ff*

Bow be-fore Him, let earth a - dore Him, For Je - sus shall reign! . . .

shall reign!

285 THE MYSTERY OF GRACE

H. L.

Haldor Lillenas

Moderato

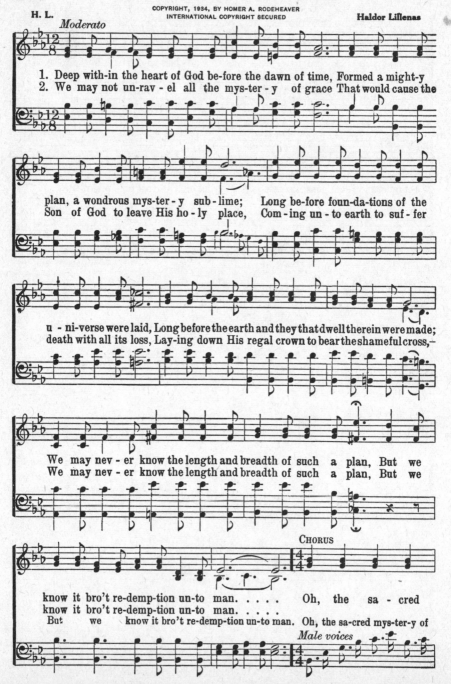

1. Deep with-in the heart of God be-fore the dawn of time, Formed a might-y
2. We may not un-rav - el all the mys-ter - y of grace That would cause the

plan, a wondrous mys-ter-y sub-lime; Long be-fore foun-da-tions of the
Son of God to leave His ho - ly place, Com-ing un - to earth to suf-fer

u - ni-verse were laid, Long before the earth and they that dwell therein were made;
death with all its loss, Lay-ing down His regal crown to bear the shameful cross,—

We may nev - er know the length and breadth of such a plan, But we
We may nev - er know the length and breadth of such a plan, But we

CHORUS

know it bro't re-demp-tion un-to man. . . . . Oh, the sa - cred
know it bro't re-demp-tion un-to man.
But we know it bro't re-demp-tion un-to man. Oh, the sa-cred mys-ter-y of

Male voices

THE MYSTERY OF GRACE

mys-ter-y of grace, Can we all its won-ders ful-ly trace?
grace, ... Can we all its won-ders ful-ly trace?. . . . .

Grace that jus-tice sat-is-fies, Grace that all our need supplies, Grace divine that can for sin a-
that

tone; . . . . . Grace, God's grace thru which we may draw near
can for sin a-tone; Grace, a-ton-ing grace thru which we may draw near

Un-to God to serve Him with-out fear, Thru this ho-ly mys-ter-y
Un-to God to serve Him without fear, ...

We from guilt have been set free, And the sons of God are we Be-cause of grace a-lone!

286 HE LIVES

A. H. A.

A. H. Ackley

1. I serve a ris - en Sav-iour, He's in the world to-day; I know that He is
2. In all the world a-round me I see His lov-ing care, And tho' my heart grows
3. Re-joice, re-joice, O Christian, lift up your voice and sing E - ter - nal hal - le-

liv - ing, what-ev - er men may say; I see His hand of mer - cy. I
wea - ry I nev - er will de - spair; I know that He is lead-ing, thru
lu - jahs to Je - sus Christ the King! The Hope of all who seek Him, the

hear His voice of cheer, And just the time I need Him He's al - ways near.
all the storm-y blast, The day of His ap pear-ing will come at last.
Help of all who find, None oth-er is so lov-ing, so good and kind.

REFRAIN *Spirited*

He lives, He lives, Christ Je-sus lives to - day! He walks with me and
He lives, He lives,

talks with me a - long life's nar-row way. He lives, He lives, sal-
He lives, He lives,

HE LIVES

va-tion to im - part! You ask me how I know He lives? He lives within my heart.

287 GOD OF OUR FATHERS

NATIONAL HYMN. 10, 10, 10, 10

Daniel C. Roberts, 1876

George W. Warren, 1892

Trumpets, before each verse.

1. God of our fa-thers, whose al-might-y hand
2. Thy love di - vine hath led us in the past,
3. From war's a-larms, from dead-ly pes - ti-lence,
4. Re - fresh Thy peo - ple on their toil-some way,

Leads forth in beau-ty all the star-ry band   Of shin-ing worlds in
In   this free land by Thee our lot is cast;   Be Thou our Rul - er,
Be   Thy strong arm our ev - er sure de-fense;   Thy true re - lig - ion
Lead us from night to nev-er-end-ing day;   Fill all our lives with

splen-dor thru the skies,   Our grate-ful songs be-fore Thy throne a - rise.
Guardian, Guide and Stay,   Thy word our law, Thy paths our cho-sen way.
in our hearts in-crease,   Thy bounteous goodness nourish us in peace.
love and grace di - vine,   And glo - ry, laud and praise be ev - er Thine.

288 A SONG OF VICTORY

Charlotte G. Homer

Chas. H. Gabriel

1. Loud - ly un - to the world is a cho - rus re-sound-ing, From the
2. Press-ing on to the bat - tle, each sol - dier re - joic - es, Sing - ing
3. Glo - ry! glo - ry to God in the high - est for - ev - er! For the

hosts of the Lord as they march a - long, Rich in har-mo-ny, send-ing the
joy - ful - ly un - to the gra-cious King; Earth is joining her praise with the
King in His beau-ty shall yet ap - pear; Shout a - loud, for Je - ho-vah, our

ech - oes re-bound-ing, Swell-ing might-i - ly from the vic - to - rious throng.
tu - mult of voic - es, While the arch-es of Heav-en with mu - sic ring.
God, will de - liv - er; His the bat - tle, and vic-to - ry draw-eth near.

CHORUS

Vic - to - ry! rings a-loud the bat-tle cry, bat-tle cry! Till the glad
Vic-to-ry! vic-to-ry! rings a-loud the bat - tle cry! . . Un-til the glo - ri-ous

ech-oes reach the vault-ed sky, vault-ed sky; O'er the world be un-furled
ech - oes reach the vault - ed sky; . . . O - ver the world now be un-furled His

A SONG OF VICTORY

now His flag from shore to shore; Loy - al, true, in the ranks each
flag from shore to shore; ... Loy-al and true, in the ranks each faith-ful

soldier stands, bravely stands, Glad - ly His will o-bey-ing in what-e'er
sol - - dier stands, .. Glad-ly o-bey-ing in what-so-ev-er He ... com-

He com-mands; He the King, the king-dom His for-ev-er-more.
mands; .. He is the King, and the king-dom His for-ev-er-more.

289 PRAISE GOD, FROM WHOM ALL BLESSINGS

Thomas Ken   OLD HUNDRED. L. M.   Louis Bourgeois

Praise God, from whom all bless-ings flow; Praise Him, all crea-tures here be - low;

Praise Him a - bove, ye heav'n-ly host; Praise Fa-ther, Son, and Ho - ly Ghost.

290 AMERICA THE BEAUTIFUL

Katharine Lee Bates

Samuel A. Ward

1. O beau-ti-ful for spa-cious skies, For am-ber waves of grain;
2. O beau-ti-ful for pil-grim feet, Whose stern, im-pas-sioned stress
3. O beau-ti-ful for he-roes proved In lib-er-at-ing strife,
4. O beau-ti-ful for pa-triot dream That sees be-yond the years

For pur-ple moun-tain maj-es-ties A-bove the fruit-ed plain!
A thor-ough-fare for free-dom beat A-cross the wil-der-ness!
Who more than self their coun-try loved, And mer-cy more than life!
Thine al-a-bas-ter cit-ies gleam Un-dimmed by hu-man tears!

A-mer-i-ca! A-mer-i-ca! God shed His grace on thee,
A-mer-i-ca! A-mer-i-ca! God mend thine ev-'ry flaw,
A-mer-i-ca! A-mer-i-ca! May God thy gold re-fine
A-mer-i-ca! A-mer-i-ca! God shed His grace on thee,

And crown thy good with broth-er-hood From sea to shin-ing sea!
Con-firm thy soul in self-con-trol, Thy lib-er-ty in law!
Till all suc-cess be no-ble-ness, And ev-'ry gain di-vine!
And crown thy good with broth-er-hood From sea to shin-ing sea!

291 MY COUNTRY, 'TIS OF THEE

Samuel Francis Smith

Attributed to Henry Carey

1. My coun-try, 'tis of thee, Sweet land of lib - er - ty,
2. My na - tive coun - try, thee, Land of the no - ble free,
3. Let mu - sic swell the breeze, And ring thru all the trees
4. Our fa - thers' God, to thee, Au - thor of lib - er - ty,

Of thee I sing; Land where my fa - thers died, Land of the
Thy name I love: I love thy rocks and rills, Thy woods and
Sweet free-dom's song; Let mor - tal tongues a - wake; Let all that
To thee we sing; Long may our land be bright With free-dom's

Pil - grim's pride, From ev - 'ry moun - tain side Let free - dom ring.
tem - pled hills; My heart with rap - ture thrills Like that a - bove.
breathe par-take; Let rocks their si - lence break, The sound pro - long.
ho - ly light: Pro - tect us by Thy might, Great God our King.

292 GLORIA PATRI

Charles Meineke

Glo - ry be to the Fa - ther, and to the Son, and to the Ho - ly Ghost; As it

was in the beginning, is now, and ev-er shall be, world without end. Amen, Amen.

293 COME, YE THANKFUL PEOPLE

Henry Alford

George J. Elvey

1. Come, ye thank-ful peo - ple, come, Raise the song of har - vest-home:
2. All the world is God's own field, Fruit un - to His praise to yield;
3. For the Lord our God shall come, And shall take His har - vest home;
4. E - ven so, Lord, quick-ly come To Thy fi - nal har - vest-home;

All is safe - ly gath - ered in, Ere the win - ter storms be - gin;
Wheat and tares to - geth - er sown, Un - to joy or sor - row grown;
From His field shall in that day All of - fens - es purge a - way;
Gath - er Thou Thy peo - ple in, Free from sor - row, free from sin;

God, our Ma - ker, doth pro - vide For our wants to be sup - plied:
First the blade, and then the ear, Then the full corn shall ap - pear:
Give His an - gels charge at last In the fire the tares to cast;
There, for - ev - er pu - ri - fied, In Thy pres-ence to a - bide:

Come to God's own tem - ple, come, Raise the song of har - vest-home.
Lord of har - vest, grant that we Wholesome grain and pure may be.
But the fruit - ful ears to store In His gar - ner ev - er-more.
Come, with all Thine an - gels, come, Raise the glo-rious har - vest-home.

294 WE PLOUGH THE FIELDS, AND SCATTER

Matthias Claudius
Translated by Jane M. Campbell

Johann A. P. Schultz

1. We plough the fields, and scat-ter The good seed on the land, But it is
2. He on - ly is the Mak - er Of all things near and far; He paints the
3. We thank Thee, then, O Fa - ther, For all things bright and good; The seed-time

fed and wa - tered By God's al-might-y hand; He sends the snow in
way-side flow - er, He lights the eve-ning star; The winds and waves o-
and the har - vest, Our life, our health, our food; No gifts have we to

win - ter, The warmth to swell the grain, The breez-es and the sun-shine,
bey Him, By Him the birds are fed; Much more to us, His chil-dren,
of - fer For all Thy love im - parts, But that which Thou de - sir - est,

REFRAIN

And soft re-fresh-ing rain.
He gives our dai - ly bread.   All good gifts a-round us Are sent from heav'n a-
Our hum-ble, thank-ful hearts.

bove; Then thank the Lord, O thank the Lord For all His love. A-MEN.

GOD BE WITH YOU

295

J. E. RANKIN

W. G. TOMER

1. God be with you till we meet a-gain; By His counsels guide, uphold you,
2. God be with you till we meet a-gain; 'Neath His wings protecting hide you,
3. God be with you till we meet a-gain; When life's perils thick confound you,
4. God be with you till we meet a-gain; Keep love's banner floating o'er you;

With His sheep se-cure-ly fold you; God be with you till we meet a-gain.
Dai - ly man-na still pro-vide you; God be with you till we meet a-gain.
Put His arms un-fail-ing round you; God be with you till we meet a-gain.
Smite death's threat'ning wave before you; God be with you till we meet a-gain.

REFRAIN

Till we meet, ... till we meet, Till we meet at Je-sus' feet;
Till we meet, till we meet, till we meet;

Till we meet, ... till we meet, God be with you till we meet a-gain.
Till we meet, till we meet,

Worship Programs
and
Responsive Readings

PREPARED BY
MRS. J. N. RODEHEAVER

WORSHIP PROGRAMS

RESPONSIVE READINGS

296 WORLD CITIZENSHIP
(Missions)

Call to Worship:

Leader:

Let us join in worshipping the heavenly Father of us all and may we remember especially those of other lands and nations.

Response:

Let us worship our King in whose name we hold our citizenship in heaven.

Hymn: "There's a Wideness in God's Mercy," Hymn 84.

Unison Prayer: Our Father, we thank Thee that we know we are Thy children. Help us to realize that all men everywhere are Thy children and our brothers. Forgive us if we have caused any of them to stumble. May our thoughts, words and deeds be evidence of our belief in the Heavenly Father and in Jesus Christ, our Savior. Amen.

Appreciation Hour: In some groups there has been an interesting service called "an appreciation hour" when various members of the group would bring some contribution from some other race or nation. A verse or song written by one from another land, some lovely handwork or art piece described by some one who knows about it and is able to tell of it in an interesting way makes a delightful and interesting story.

Reading *(without music):* "In Christ There Is No East or West," Hymn 226.
First stanza:

"In Christ there is no East or West,
In Him no South or North;
But one great fellowship of love
Throughout the whole wide earth."

Second stanza (read by Leader):

"In Him shall true hearts ev'rywhere
Their high communion find;
His service is the golden cord
Close-binding all mankind."

Third and Fourth stanzas (sung by entire group):

"Join hands then, brothers of the faith,
Whate'er your race may be;
Who serves My Father as a son
Is surely kin to Me.

In Christ now meet both East and West,
In Him meet South and North;
All Christly souls are one in Him
Throughout the whole wide earth."

297   **PATRIOTIC**

Instrumental Call to Worship: "God of Our Fathers," Hymn 287.

Hymn of Praise *(sung by all):* "God of Our Fathers."

Unison: OUR GREAT LEADER, be with us this day as we remember with reverence those who have given their lives and their strength that we might live in a better country. May they not have died in vain. Help us to follow in their footsteps by our consecration to the ideals of the Prince of Peace. In the name of Jesus, our Savior, we ask it. Amen.

Scripture *(Responsive reading):*

> Therefore thou shalt keep the commandments of the Lord thy God, to walk in His ways and fear Him.
>
> **For the Lord, thy God, bringeth thee into a good land, a land of brooks of water, of fountains and depths that spring out of valleys and hills;**
>
> A land of wheat and barley and vines, and fig trees, and pomegrantes; a land of oil olive, and honey;
>
> **A land wherein thou shalt eat bread without scarceness, thou shalt not lack anything in it; a land whose stones are iron, and out of whose hills thou mayest dig brass.**
>
> When thou hast eaten and art full, then thou shalt bless the Lord thy God for the good land which He hath given thee.
>
> **But thou shalt remember the Lord thy God: for it is He that giveth thee power to get wealth? that He may establish His covenant which He sware unto thy fathers? as it is this day. (Deut. 8:6-18.)**

Salute to the American Flag: "I pledge allegiance to the flag of the United States of America and to the Republic for which it stands; one Nation indivisible, with liberty and justice for all."

Hymn: "America," Hymn 291.

Salute to the Christian Flag: "I pledge allegiance to the Christian flag and the Savior for whose kingdom it stands, one brotherhood uniting all mankind in service and love."

Hymn: "Jesus Shall Reign" (Duke Street), Hymn 221.

298   THANKFUL HEARTS
(Thanksgiving)

Hymn of Rejoicing: "For the Beauty of the Earth," Hymn 75.

Silent Prayer of Thankful Hearts.

Unison Prayer: Dear Lord, we come to this service to give thanks to Thee for the many gifts to us. We acknowledge Thee as the giver of all gifts, not only those which feed and clothe our bodies but also those which bring extra joy and richness into our lives. We thank Thee most of all for the joy of Christian fellowship and we ask Thee to bless us as we meet here together this day. Amen.

Responsive Reading: Psalm 65, verses 9-13, number 320.

Hymn of Gratitude: "Come Ye Thankful People Come," Hymn 293.

Leader (reading):

>Come, ye thankful people come,
>Raise the song of harvest-home;
>All is safely gathered in,
>Ere the winter storms begin;
>God, our Maker, doth provide
>For the wants to be supplied:
>Come to God's own temple, come,
>Raise the song of harvest home.

Audience (reading):

>**All the world is God's own field,**
>**Fruit unto His praise to yield;**
>**Wheat and tares together sown**
>**Unto joy or sorrow grown;**
>**First the blade and then the ear,**
>**Then the full corn shall appear:**
>**Lord of harvest grant that we**
>**Wholesome grain and pure may be.**

Third and Fourth Stanzas to Be Sung by All.

(Story, from "Special Days in the Church School" by Margaret Eggelston. "Ahni," page 64.)

Closing Hymn: "Sweet Peace, the Gift of God's Love," Hymn 178.

299 ## INSTALLATION SERVICE
(For the Officers of the Various Church Organizations)

Instrumental Music: "Give of Your Best to the Master," Hymn 123.

Leader:
We have met here to pledge our allegiance to our Master in whose name we are called to serve. You have been honored by your fellow members who ask you to accept the responsibility of leadership in (name of the organization). May you ask God's blessing on the work which you are called to do.

Prayer—By Officers Elect:
Our Father, we ask Thee to be with us as we enter upon the duties of leadership. We realize that our own strength is not sufficient, but we know that Thou art able to meet every need. In Thy strength we go forward. Let Thy blessing be upon us as we strive to serve. In Jesus' name we ask it. Amen.

Leader:
You have accepted the office to which you have been elected, and have asked God's blessing upon you as you enter this service. Do you solemnly promise to fulfill the duties of your office to the best of your ability, relying upon God to direct and guide you?

Officers (in unison, or singly):
I do.

Song: "I Would Be True," Hymn 106.

Leader (addressing audience):
You have heard your leaders promise to faithfully fulfill the duties of the offices to which you have elected them. A true leader can do only as much as faithful followers permit. Will you pledge to your officers your hearty support and assistance as they work with you in the interest of this organization?

Audience:
We will.

Consecration Hymn: "O Jesus I have Promised," Hymn 254.

Prayer of Consecration *(by all):* Our Heavenly Guide, we have given our pledge before our friends and Thee to do our work as leaders and followers. Help us to be faithful to this pledge. We rely upon Thy strength and power and ask Thee to go with each one of us as we go out to carry on the task for Thy kingdom. Help us to see only Jesus Christ, our Saviour, and may His Desire for our lives be our great compelling force. Amen.

Request for Guidance—Song: "Lead On O King Eternal," Hymn 124.

300 THE RISEN CHRIST
(Easter)

Meditation as Music is played softly: "Softly and Tenderly," Hymn 274.
Hymn of Rejoicing: "Christ Arose," Hymn 238.
Scripture Reading—Responsive:

Leader:
> Now upon the first day of the week, very early in the morning, they came unto the sepulchre, bringing the spices which they had prepared, and certain others with them.

Audience:
> **And they found the stone rolled away from the sepulchre.**

Leader:
> And they entered in, and found not the body of the Lord Jesus.

Audience:
> **And it came to pass, as they were much perplexed thereabout, behold, two men stood by them, why seek ye the living among the dead?**

Leader:
> He is not here, but is risen; remember how He spake unto you when He was yet in Galilee, saying, The Son of man must be delivered into the hands of sinful men, and be crucified, and the third day rise again.

Audience:
> **And they remembered His words, and returned from the sepulchre, and told all these things unto the eleven and to all the rest.**

Hymn: "Crown Him with Many Crowns," Hymn 239.
> (*Suggested Story:* "At Easter Time" from "Stories for Special Days in the Church School," by Margaret Eggelston, or "The Boy Who Found the Spring" from "Why the Chimes Rang" (complete edition), by Raymond MacDonald Alden.)

Declaration:

Leader:
> We see the spring bringing to us the newly awakened buds

Audience:
> **We know that Christ arose.**

Leader:
> We see the redeemed lives of those who were unaware of life's great opportunities and possibilities

Audience:
> **We know that Christ arose.**

Leader:
> We call upon His name for strength in our tasks

Audience:
> **We know that Christ arose and because He lives we too shall live.**

Benediction.

301   MOTHER'S DAY

Music *(softly):* "I Would Be True," Hymn 106.

Unison: Our Father, as we enter upon this day made sacred by the memories which flood our lives with joy and peace, grant that we may realize our debt to those who held high the torch of faith and may gain new inspiration to go forward. Amen.

Music: "I Would Be True," Hymn 106 (first stanza).

Recitation *(Mother):*

> The noblest thoughts my soul can claim,
> The holiest words my tongue can frame,
> Unworthy are to praise the name
> > More sacred than all other.
> An infant when her love first came—
> A man, I find it just the same;
> Reverently I breathe her name,
> > The blessed name of mother.

Prayer for Guidance:

Leader:
> Our Father who art in Heaven, we thank Thee for the Christian Mothers. As they lighted our pathway in our tender years

Audience:
> **May we light the path for the children of this day**

Leader:
> As they led us to Thy feet in prayer

Audience:
> **May we lead our children to Thy feet in prayer.**

Leader:
> As they guided us in ways of righteousness and service

Audience:
> **May we lead others. May we be true to the highest ideals which they taught us. Help us to be worthy sons and daughters. In Jesus' Name we ask it. Amen.**

Music: "I Would Be True," Hymn 106 (second stanza sung as a solo if possible).

> (Story from "Stories for Special Days in the Church School," by Margaret W. Eggleston. Page 90.)

Song: "Give of Your Best to the Master," Hymn 123.

302   HOME COMING

Musical Prelude: "Faith of Our Fathers," Hymn 25.

Call to Prayer:
Leader:
> As we gather here today memories flood in upon us. We remember the family pew where we worshipped with our loved ones. We remember the hosts of friends who shared our joys and sorrows. Let us thank God for His presence through all of life's experiences.

Responsive Prayer:
Leader (in light-face type):
Audience (in bold-face type):
> For the memories of happy associations
> **We thank Thee O Lord.**
> For our own loved ones
> **We thank Thee O Lord.**
> For Thy presence in sorrow and heartache
> **We thank Thee O Lord.**
> For Thy blessing in our hours of joy
> **We thank Thee O Lord.**
> For loved friends who remain to share this hour
> **We thank Thee O Lord.**
> For the memory and ever present influence of those who have gone to their heavenly homes
> **We thank Thee O Lord. As they have been a blessing to us, may we be a blessing to others. Amen.**

Praise Through Song: "Blest Be the Tie That Binds," Hymn 224.

From the Word of God:
Leader (in light-face type):
Audience (in bold-face type):
> THE LORD is the portion of mine inheritance and of my cup: Thou maintainest my lot.
> **The lines are fallen unto me in pleasant places; yea, I have a goodly heritage.**
> I will bless the Lord, who hath given me counsel; my reins also instruct me in the night seasons.
> **I have set the Lord always before me: because He is at my right hand, I shall not be moved.**
> **ALL: Thou wilt show me the path of life: in Thy presence is fulness of joy: at Thy right hand there are pleasures for evermore.**

Two or three short talks on "Radiant Personalities in This Community Yester day and Today."

Benediction in Song: "God Be With You Till We Meet Again," Hymn 295.

303   OUR GUIDE
(The Bible)

Call to Worship: "Wonderful Words of Life," Hymn 194.
(Stanzas sung as solo, chorus by entire group.)

Unison Prayer: We praise Thee O God for this guide book which shows us the course we must follow every step of the way. Help us to be more earnest as students of Thy word. Amen.

What Great Leaders Have Said About the Bible *(to be given as assigned by the Leader):*

1. Daniel Webster, who read the Bible through once a year, said, "If we abide by the principles taught in the Bible our country will go on prospering and to prosper, but if we and our posterity neglect its instructions and authority no man can tell how sudden a catastrophe may overwhelm us."
2. At ten years of age Abraham Lincoln had read the Bible through three times. He said, "All the good from the Saviour of the world is communicated through this Book; but for this Book we could not know right from wrong. All things desirable to man are contained in it."
3. Coleridge said, "The Bible finds me as no other book does."
4. Horace Greeley said, "It is impossible to mentally or socially enslave a Bible-reading people."
5. A Chinese professor said, "I have studied all the great religions of the world. When I came to study the Bible and the life of Jesus, I found in him all the truth of the other religions, and so much more besides, that if I can only take Jesus back to China, China will be saved."

Praise Through Song: "Thy Word, O Lord, Is My Delight," Hymn 57.

Responsive Prayer:

> *Leader:*
> For Thy Word, which is in truth a lamp unto our feet.
> *Audience:*
> **We thank Thee O Lord.**
> *Leader:*
> For the great promises which it contains
> *Audience:*
> **We praise Thee O Lord.**
> *Leader:*
> For the beauty of it
> *Audience:*
> **We give Thee Thanks.**
> *Leader:*
> For the comfort it brings
> *Audience:*
> **We bow our heads and hearts in sincere gratitude.**
> *Leader:*
> For the will to study it earnestly
> *Audience:*
> **We ask Thy blessing.**

Benediction in Song: "O Word of God Incarnate," Hymn 60.

304   BE BORN IN US TODAY
(Christmas)

Music *(played softly)*: "O Little Town of Bethlehem," Hymn 230.

Responsive Prayer:

Leader:
> "O holy child of Bethlehem
> Descend on us we pray
> Cast out our sin and enter in
> Be born in us today."

Audience:
> **Be born in us today.**

Leader:
> "We hear the Christmas angels
> The great glad tidings tell,
> O come to us, abide with us,
> Our Lord Emmanuel." ·

Audience:
> **Be born in us today.**

Hymn *(sung antiphonally)*: "Joy to the World," Hymn 231.

Men:	Joy to the world; the Lord is come
Women:	Let earth receive her king
Men:	Let every heart prepare him room
Women:	And heav'n and nature sing,
Men:	And heav'n and nature sing,
ALL:	And heav'n, and heav'n and nature sing.

Scripture Reading: For Christmas, number 322.

Song Story *(sung by the audience)*: "While Shepherds Watched," Hymn 236.

First Stanza: Sung by the men.
Second Stanza: Sung by the boys.
Third Stanza: Sung by the women.
Fourth Stanza: Sung by the girls.
Fifth Stanza: Sung by all.

Closing Prayer *(unison)*: O holy child of Bethlehem, be born in us today. Let us so live that others may know we have invited Thee to dwell with us and to share our homes, our work and every activity that claims our time. With gratitude for the wonderful gift, we ask it. Amen.

305   JESUS THE LEADER
(Rally Day)

Prayer: Dear Lord, be Thou our guide as we walk the pathway of life. Be Thou the light which shines before our footsteps that we may walk the way of life. May we let nothing come in which will make that light shine dimly because we placed a cloud there. Help us to keep our eyes steadfastly turned toward that light and to follow in it. Amen.

Leader:
> The Lord is my light and my salvation.

Audience:
> **Whom shall I fear?**

Song of Light: "Lamp of Our Feet," Hymn 58, First Stanza.

> Lamp of our feet, whereby we trace
> Our path when won't to stray;
> Stream from the fount of heav'nly grace,
> Brook by the trav'ler's way.

Leader:
> The Lord is the strength of my life

Audience:
> **Of whom shall I be afraid?**

Leader:
> Jesus said: "Ye are the light of the earth"

Audience:
> **Help us O God to hold high the torch which has been handed to us by Jesus Christ, our light, our strength and our salvation. Amen.**

Leader:
> Jesus said, "I am the bread of life."

Response in Song: "Lamp of Our Feet," Second Stanza.

> Bread of our souls, whereon we feed
> True manna from on high;
> Our guide and chart, wherein we read
> Of realms beyond the sky.

(*Suggested Story:* "The Life Saver" or "Two Steps Forward" from "Stories for Special Days in the Church School," Margaret Eggleston.)

Song Prayer for Guidance: "Guide Me, O Thou Great Jehovah," Hymn 21.

Silent Prayer: For guidance in personal needs.

Unison Prayer: We pray with all sincerity that Thou wilt truly guide us, our Savior, our Light, our Strength. May we be faithful followers in the path our Master treads. In His name we ask it. Amen.

306 THE DAY IS DONE
(Evening)

Music *(softly)*: "Day Is Dying in the West," Hymn 44. To be played softly as the audience reads the words silently, then all join in singing quietly.

Call to Worship: As we come to the eventide, let us seek the presence of our Master, who brings peace to those who abide with him.

Prayer: Our Father, we have come to the eventide and now we pause to commune with Thee. May this be a time of quiet in which we may hear Thy voice. May Thy blessing rest upon the worthy tasks which we have done this day. May Thy forgiveness blot out the unworthy deeds which we have committed. Grant us Thy blessing during the night. Forgive us if we are responsible for making it necessary for one of Thy children to go to bed hungry, or with a heartache tonight. Help us to gather strength to live tomorrow in such a way that we may bring happiness to those who need us. Amen.

Prayer of Communion: "An Evening Prayer, Hymn 81, sung as a solo if possible.

Response in Song *(by audience)*: "Softly Now the Light of Day," Hymn 46.

A Sharing of Sunset Experiences. Let several tell of some especially impressive evening service which they have experienced. It may be the quiet communing of kindred minds such as comes when good friends watch the setting of the sun without speaking a word, or a vesper service held beside the lake at some summer assembly, a mountain top experience, a Galilean service, the southern cross nights of India or the northern lights of northern Europe and America. It would be well to assign these topics before the meeting, but allowing time for those who may wish to speak extemporaneously to share their beautiful memories which form "life's extras."

Closing Hymn of Quiet Worship: "Now the Day Is Over," Hymn 45.

First Stanza: To be read silently as the organist plays the music.
Second Stanza: To be sung by the men.
Third Stanza: To be sung by the women.
Fourth Stanza: To be sung by all.
Fifth Stanza: To be read silently as the organist plays the music.

Leader:
This is the prayer of our hearts, our Heavenly Father, and we ask Thee to hear it

Audience:
And go with us every step of the way. Amen.

307 SING UNTO THE LORD
Psalm 96

Oh, sing unto the Lord a new song; sing unto the Lord, all the earth.

Sing unto the Lord, bless his name; show forth his salvation from day to day.

Declare his glory among the heathen, his wonders among all people.

For the Lord is great, and greatly to be praised: he is to be feared above all gods.

For all the gods of the nations are idols: but the Lord made the heavens.

Honor and majesty are before him; strength and beauty are in his sanctuary.

Give unto the Lord, O ye kindreds of the people, give unto the Lord glory and strength.

Give unto the Lord the glory due unto his name: bring an offering and come into his courts.

Oh, worship the Lord in the beauty of holiness: fear before him, all the earth.

Say among the heathen that the Lord reigneth:

The world also shall be established that it shall not be moved: he shall judge the people righteously.

Let the heavens rejoice, and let the earth be glad; let the sea roar, and the fullness thereof.

Let the field be joyful, and all that is therein:

Then shall all the trees of the wood rejoice before the Lord:

For he cometh, for he cometh to judge the earth:

He shall judge the world with righteousness, and the people with his truth.

308 GOD IN NATURE
Psalm 19

The heavens declare the glory of God; and the firmament sheweth his handiwork.

Day unto day uttereth speech, and night unto night sheweth knowledge.

There is no speech nor language, where the voice is not heard.

Their line is gone out through all the earth, and their words to the end of the world. In them hath he set a tabernacle for the sun.

Which is as a bridegroom coming out of his chamber, and rejoiceth as a strong man to run a race.

His going forth is from the end of the heaven, and his circuit unto the ends of it: and there is nothing hid from the heat thereof.

The law of the Lord is perfect, converting the soul: the testimony of the Lord is sure, making wise the simple.

The statutes of the Lord are right, rejoicing the heart: the commandment of the Lord is pure, enlightening the eyes.

The fear of the Lord is clean, enduring forever: the judgments of the Lord are true and righteous altogether.

More to be desired are they than gold, yea, than much fine gold: sweeter also than honey and the honey-comb.

Moreover by them is thy servant warned: and in keeping of them there is great reward.

Who can understand his errors? cleanse thou me from secret faults.

Keep back thy servant also from presumptuous sins; let them not have dominion over me; then shall I be upright, and I shall be innocent from the great transgression.

Let the words of my mouth, and the meditation of my heart, be acceptable in thy sight, O Lord, my strength, and my redeemer.

309 THE LIVING CHRIST
John 20:6-18

Then cometh Simon Peter following him, and went into the sepulchre, and seeth the linen clothes lie,

And the napkin, that was about his head, not lying with the linen clothes, but wrapped together in a place by itself.

Then went in also that other disciple, which came first to the sepulchre, and he saw and believed.

For as yet they knew not the scripture, that he must rise again from the dead.

Then the disciples went away again unto their own home.

But Mary stood without at the sepulchre weeping: and as she wept, she stooped down, and looked into the sepulchre,

And seeth two angels in white sitting, the one at the head, and the other at the feet, where the body of Jesus had lain.

And they say unto her, Woman, why weepest thou? She saith unto them, Because they have taken away my Lord, and I know not where they have laid him.

And when she had thus said, she turned herself back, and saw Jesus standing, and knew not that it was Jesus.

Jesus saith unto her, Woman, why weepest thou? Whom seekest thou?

She, supposing him to be the gardener, saith unto him, Sir, if thou have borne him hence, tell me where thou hast laid him, and I will take him away.

Jesus saith unto her, Mary. She turned herself, and saith unto him, Rabboni; which is to say, Master.

Jesus saith unto her, Touch me not; for I am not yet ascended to my Father: but go to my brethren, and say unto them, I ascend unto my Father, and your Father; and to my God and your God.

Mary Magdalene came and told the disciples that she had seen the Lord, and that he had spoken these things unto her.

310 BROTHERLY KINDNESS
Gal. 6:1-10

Brethren, if a man be overtaken in a fault, ye which are spiritual, restore such an one in the spirit of meekness; considering thyself, lest thou also be tempted.

Bear ye one another's burdens and so fulfil the law of Christ.

For if a man think himself to be something, when he is nothing, he deceiveth himself.

But let every man prove his own work, and then shall he have rejoicing in himself alone, and not in another.

For every man shall bear his own burden.

Let him that is taught in the Word communicate unto him that teacheth in all good things.

Be not deceived; God is not mocked: for whatsoever a man soweth, that shall he also reap.

For he that soweth to his flesh shall of the flesh reap corruption; but he that soweth to the Spirit shall of the Spirit reap life everlasting.

And let us not be weary in well doing: for in due season we shall reap, if we faint not.

As we have therefore opportunity, let us do good unto all men especially unto them who are of the household of faith.

311 THE NEW BIRTH
John 3:1-16

There was a man of the Pharisees, named Nicodemus, a ruler of the Jews:

The same came to Jesus by night, and said unto him, Rabbi, we know that Thou art a teacher come from God: for no man can do these miracles that Thou doest, except God be with him.

Jesus answered and said unto him, Verily, verily, I say unto thee, Except a man be born again, he cannot see the kingdom of God.

Nicodemus saith unto him, How can a man be born when he is old? Can he enter the second time into his mother's womb, and be born?

Jesus answered, Verily, verily, I say unto thee, Except a man be born of water and of the Spirit, he cannot enter into the kingdom of God.

That which is born of the flesh is flesh; and that which is born of the Spirit is spirit.

Marvel not that I said unto thee, Ye must be born again.

The wind bloweth where it listeth, and thou hearest the sound thereof, but canst not tell whence it cometh, and whither it goeth: so is every one that is born of the Spirit.

Nicodemus answered and said unto Him, How can these things be?

Jesus answered and said unto him, Art thou a master of Israel, and knowest not these things?

Verily, verily, I say unto thee, We speak that we do know, and testify that we have seen; and ye receive not our witness.

If I have told you earthly things, and ye believe not, how shall ye believe, if I tell you of heavenly things?

And no man hath ascended up to heaven, but he that came down from heaven, even the Son of man which is in heaven.

And as Moses lifted up the serpent in the wilderness, even so must the Son of man be lifted up:

That whosoever believeth in him should not perish, but have eternal life.

For God so loved the world, that he gave his only begotten Son, that whosoever believeth in him should not perish but have everlasting life.

312 GOD IS OUR REFUGE
Psalms 46:1-11

God is our refuge and strength, a very present help in trouble.

Therefore will not we fear, though the earth be removed, and though the mountains be carried into the midst of the sea;

Though the waters thereof roar and be troubled, though the mountains shake with the swelling thereof.

There is a river, the streams whereof shall make glad the city of God, the holy place of the Tabernacles of the Most High.

God is in the midst of her; she shall not be moved; God shall help her, and that right early.

The heathen raged, the kingdoms were moved: he uttered his voice, the earth melted.

The Lord of hosts is with us; the God of Jacob is our refuge.

Come, behold the works of the Lord, what desolations he hath made in the earth.

He maketh wars to cease unto the end of the earth; he breaketh the bow, and cutteth the spear in sunder; he burneth the chariot in the fire.

Be still, and know that I am God: I will be exalted among the heathen, I will be exalted in the earth.

The Lord of hosts is with us; the God of Jacob is our refuge.

313   THIRST FOR GOD
Psalms 42:1-11

As the hart panteth after the water brooks, so panteth my soul after thee, O God.

My soul thirsteth for God, for the living God: when shall I come and appear before God?

My tears have been my meat day and night, while they continually say unto me, Where is thy God?

When I remember these things, I pour out my soul in me: for I had gone with the multitude, I went with them to the house of God with the voice of joy and praise, with a multitude that kept holyday.

Why art thou cast down, O my soul? and why art thou disquieted in me? hope thou in God: for I shall yet praise him for the help of his countenance.

O my God, my soul is cast down within me: therefore will I remember thee from the land of Jordan, and of the Hermonites, from the Hill Mizar.

Deep calleth unto deep at the noise of thy waterspouts: all thy waves and thy billows are gone over me.

Yet the Lord will command his lovingkindness in the daytime, and in the night his song shall be with me, and my prayer unto the God of my life.

I will say unto God my rock, Why hast thou forgotten me? who go I mourning because of the oppression of the enemy?

As with a sword in my bones, mine enemies reproach me; while they say daily unto me, where is thy God?

Why art thou cast down, O my soul? and why art thou disquieted within me?

Hope thou in God; for I shall yet praise him, who is the health of my countenance, and my God.

314   BEATITUDES
Matthew 5:3-16

Blessed are the poor in spirit:
For theirs is the kingdom of heaven.
Blessed are they that mourn:
For they shall be comforted.
Blessed are the meek:
For they shall inherit the earth.

Blessed are they which do hunger and thirst after righteousness:

For they shall be filled.

Blessed are the merciful:
For they shall obtain mercy.
Blessed are the pure in heart:
For they shall see God.
Blessed are the peacemakers:

For they shall be called the children of God.

Blessed are they which are persecuted for righteousness' sake:

For theirs is the kingdom of heaven.

Blessed are ye, when men shall revile you, and persecute you,

And shall say all manner of evil against you falsely for my sake.

Rejoice, and be exceeding glad: for great is your reward in heaven.

For so persecuted they the prophets which were before you.

Ye are the salt of the earth. Ye are the light of the world.

Let your light so shine before men, that they may see your good works, and glorify your Father which is in heaven.

315 THE GREATEST GIFT
I Cor. 13:1-13

Though I speak with the tongues of men and of angels, and have not charity, I am become as sounding brass, or a tinkling cymbal.

And though I have the gift of prophecy, and understand all mysteries, and all knowledge; and though I have all faith, so that I could remove mountains, and have not charity, I am nothing.

And though I bestow all my goods to feed the poor, and though I give my body to be burned, and have not charity, it profiteth me nothing.

Charity suffereth long, and is kind; charity envieth not; charity vaunteth not itself, is not puffed up,

Doth not behave itself unseemly, seeketh not her own, is not easily provoked, thinketh no evil;

Rejoiceth not in iniquity, but rejoiceth in the truth;

Beareth all things, believeth all things, hopeth all things, endureth all things.

Charity never faileth: but whether there be prophecies, they shall fail; whether there be tongues, they shall cease; whether there be knowledge, it shall vanish away.

For we know in part, and we prophesy in part.

But when that which is perfect is come, then that which is in part shall be done away.

When I was a child, I spake as a child, I understood as a child, I thought as a child: but when I became a man, I put away childish things.

For now we see through a glass darkly; but then face to face: now I know in part; but then shall I know even as also I am known.

And now abideth faith, hope, charity, these three; but the greatest of these is charity.

316 PRAISE AND WORSHIP
Psalms 84:1-10; Psalms 100:1-4

How amiable are thy tabernacles, O Lord of hosts!

My soul longeth, yea, even fainteth for the courts of the Lord; my heart and my flesh crieth out for the living God.

Yea, the sparrow hath found an house, and the swallow a nest for herself, where she may lay her young, even thine altars, O Lord of hosts, my King, and my God.

Blessed are they that dwell in thy house: they will be still praising thee.

Blessed is the man whose strength is in thee; in whose heart are the ways of them.

Who passing through the Valley of Baca make it a well; the rain also filleth the pools.

They go from strength to strength, every one of them in Zion appeareth before God.

O Lord God of hosts, hear my prayer: give ear, O God of Jacob.

Behold, O God our shield, and look upon the face of thine anointed.

For a day in thy courts is better than a thousand. I had rather be a doorkeeper in the house of my God, than to dwell in the tents of wickedness.

Make a joyful noise unto the Lord, all ye lands.

Serve the Lord with gladness: come before His presence with singing.

Know ye that the Lord he is God: it is he that hath made us and not we ourselves; we are his people, and the sheep of his pasture.

Enter into his gates with thanksgiving, and into his courts with praise: be thankful unto him, and bless his name.

317   DECISION
Matt. 4:1-11; 17-22

Then was Jesus led up of the Spirit into the wilderness to be tempted of the devil.

And when he had fasted forty days and forty nights, he was afterward an hungered.

And when the tempter came to Him, he said, If thou be the Son of God, command that these stones be made bread.

But he answered and said, It is written, man shall not live by bread alone, but by every word that proceedeth out of the mouth of God.

Then the devil taketh him up into the holy city, and setteth him on a pinnacle of the temple,

And saith unto him, If thou be the Son of God, cast thyself down: for it is written, He shall give his angels charge concerning thee: and in their hands they shall bear thee up, lest at any time thou dash thy foot against a stone.

Jesus said unto him, It is written again, Thou shalt not tempt the Lord thy God.

Again, the devil taketh him up into an exceeding high mountain, and sheweth him all the kingdoms of the world, and the glory of them;

And saith unto him, All these things will I give thee, if thou wilt fall down and worship me.

Then saith Jesus unto him, Get thee hence, Satan: For it is written, thou shalt worship the Lord thy God, and him only shalt thou serve.

Then the devil leaveth him, and, behold, angels came and ministered unto him.

From that time Jesus began to preach, and to say, Repent: for the kingdom of heaven is at hand.

And Jesus, walking by the Sea of Galilee, saw two brethren, Simon called Peter, and Andrew his brother, casting a net into the sea; for they were fishers.

And he saith unto them, Follow me, and I will make you fishers of men.

And they straightway left their nets, and followed him.

318   THE KING OF GLORY
Psalms 95:1-6; Psalms 24:3-10

O come let us sing unto the Lord: let us make a joyful noise to the rock of our salvation.

Let us come before his presence with thanksgiving, and make a joyful noise unto him with psalms.

For the Lord is a great God, and a great King above all gods.

In his hand are the deep places of the earth: the strength of the hills is his also.

The sea is his, and he made it; and His hands formed the dry land.

O come, let us worship and bow down: let us kneel before the Lord our Maker.

Who shall ascend into the hill of the Lord? or who shall stand in his holy place?

He that hath clean hands, and a pure heart; who hath not lifted up his soul unto vanity, nor sworn deceitfully.

He shall receive the blessing from the Lord, and righteousness from the God of his salvation.

Lift up your head, O ye gates; and be ye lifted up, ye everlasting doors; and the King of glory shall come in.

Who is this King of glory?

The Lord strong and mighty, the Lord mighty in battle.

Lift up your heads, O ye gates;

Even lift them up, ye everlasting doors; and the King of glory shall come in.

Who is this King of glory?

The Lord of hosts, he is the King of glory.

319 THANKSGIVING AND PRAISE

Psalm 34

I will bless the Lord at all times; his praise shall continually be in my mouth.

My soul shall make her boast in the Lord: the humble shall hear thereof, and be glad.

O magnify the Lord with me, and let us exalt his name together.

I sought the Lord, and he heard me, and delivered me from all my fears.

They looked unto him, and were lightened: and their faces were not ashamed.

This poor man cried, and the Lord heard him, and saved him out of all his troubles.

The angel of the Lord encampeth round about them that fear him, and delivereth them.

O taste and see that the Lord is good: blessed is the man that trusteth in him.

O fear the Lord, ye His saints: for there is no want to them that fear him.

The young lions do lack, and suffer hunger: but they that seek the Lord shall not want any good thing.

Come, ye children, hearken unto me: I will teach you the fear of the Lord.

What man is he that desireth life, and loveth many days, that he may see good?

Keep thy tongue from evil, and thy lips from speaking guile.

Depart from evil, and do good; seek peace, and pursue it.

The eyes of the Lord are upon the righteous, and his ears are open unto their cry.

The face of the Lord is against them that do evil, to cut off the remembrance of them from the earth.

The righteous cry, and the Lord heareth, and delivereth them out of all their troubles.

The Lord is nigh unto them that are of a broken heart; and saveth such as be of a contrite spirit.

Many are the afflictions of the righteous: but the Lord delivereth him out of them all.

He keepeth all his bones: not one of them is broken.

Evil shall slay the wicked; and they that hate the righteous shall be desolate.

The Lord redeemeth the soul of his servants: and none of them that trust in him shall be desolate.

320 THANKSGIVING AND PRAISE

Psalms 65:9-13

Thou visitest the earth, and waterest it: thou greatly enrichest it with the river of God, which is full of water:

Thou preparest them corn, when thou hast so provided for it.

Thou waterest the ridges thereof abundantly: thou settlest the furrows thereof: thou makest it soft with showers: thou blessest the springing thereof.

Thou crownest the year with thy goodness; and thy paths drop fatness.

They drop upon the pastures of the wilderness: and the little hills rejoice on every side.

The pastures are clothed with flocks; the valleys also are covered over with corn; they shout for joy, they also sing.

321   GOD'S CARE
Psalms 23 and 27

The Lord is my shepherd; I shall not want.

He maketh me to lie down in green pastures.

He leadeth me beside the still waters.

He restoreth my soul:

He leadeth me in the paths of righteousness for his name's sake.

Yea, though I walk through the valley of the shadow of death, I will fear no evil: for thou art with me;

Thy rod and thy staff they comfort me.

Thou preparest a table before me in the presence of mine enemies: thou anointest mine head with oil; my cup runneth over.

Surely goodness and mercy shall follow me all the days of my life; and I will dwell in the house of the Lord forever.

The Lord is my light and my salvation; whom shall I fear?

The Lord is the strength of my life; of whom shall I be afraid?

Though an host should encamp against me, my heart shall not fear:

Though war should rise against me, in this will I be confident.

For in the time of trouble he shall hide me in his pavilion:

In the secret of His tabernacle shall he hide me; he shall set me up upon a rock.

And now shall my head be lifted up above mine enemies round about me: therefore will I offer in his tabernacle sacrifices of joy:

I will sing, yea, I will sing praises unto the Lord.

When my father and my mother forsake me, then the Lord will take me up.

I had fainted, unless I had believed to see the goodness of the Lord in the land of the living.

Wait on the Lord: be of good courage, and he shall strengthen thine heart: wait, I say, on the Lord.

322   CHRISTMAS
Luke 2:8-20

And there were in the same country shepherds abiding in the field, keeping watch over their flock by night.

And, lo, the angel of the Lord came upon them, and the glory of the Lord shone round about them: and they were sore afraid.

And the angel said unto them, Fear not: for, behold, I bring you good tidings of great joy, which shall be to all people.

For unto you is born this day in the city of David a Saviour, which is Christ the Lord.

And this shall be a sign unto you; Ye shall find the babe wrapped in swaddling clothes, lying in a manger.

And suddenly there was with the angel a multitude of the heavenly host praising God, and saying,

Glory to God in the highest, and on earth peace, good will toward men.

And it came to pass, as the angels were gone away from them into heaven, the shepherds said one to another, Let us now go even unto Bethlehem, and see this thing which is come to pass, which the Lord hath made known unto us.

And they came with haste, and found Mary, and Joseph, and the babe lying in a manger.

And when they had seen it, they made known abroad the saying which was told them concerning this child.

And all they that heard it wondered at those things which were told them by the shepherds.

But Mary kept all these things, and pondered them in her heart.

323 PATRIOTIC
Deut. 8:6-19

Therefore thou shalt keep the commandments of the Lord thy God, to walk in his ways, and to fear him.

For the Lord thy God bringeth thee into a good land, a land of brooks of water, of fountains and depths, that spring out of valleys and hills;

A land of wheat and barley, and vines, and fig trees and pomegranates; a land of oil olive, and honey.

A land wherein thou shalt eat bread without scarceness, thou shalt not lack any thing in it; a land whose stones are iron, and out of whose hills thou mayest dig brass.

When thou hast eaten and art full, then thou shalt bless the Lord thy God for the good land which he hath given thee.

Beware that thou forget not the Lord thy God, in not keeping His commandments, and his judgments, and his statutes, which I command thee this day:

Lest when thou hast eaten and art full, and hast built goodly houses, and dwelt therein;

And when thy herds and thy flocks multiply, and thy silver and thy gold is multiplied, and all that thou hast is multiplied;

Then thine heart be lifted up, and thou forget the Lord thy God, which brought thee forth out of the land of Egypt, from the house of bondage;

Who led thee through that great and terrible wilderness, wherein were fiery serpents, and scorpions, and drought, where there was no water; who brought thee forth water out of the rock of flint;

Who fed thee in the wilderness with manna, which thy fathers knew not, that he might humble thee, and that He might prove thee, to do thee good at thy latter end;

And thou say in thine heart, my power and the might of mine hand hath gotten me this wealth.

But thou shalt remember the Lord thy God; for it is he that giveth thee power to get wealth, that he may establish His covenant which he sware unto thy fathers, as it is this day.

And it shall be, if thou do at all forget the Lord thy God, and walk after other gods, and serve them, and worship them, I testify against you this day that ye shall surely perish.

324 THE WHOLE ARMOUR
Eph. 6:10-18

Finally, my brethren, be strong in the Lord, and in the power of his might.

Put on the whole armour of God, that ye may be able to stand against the wiles of the devil.

For we wrestle not against flesh and blood, but against principalities, against powers, against the rulers of the darkness of this world, against spiritual wickedness in high places.

Wherefore take unto you the whole armour of God, that ye may be able to withstand in the evil day, and having done all, to stand.

Stand, therefore, having your loins girt about with truth, and having on the breastplate of righteousness;

And your feet shod with the preparation of the gospel of peace;

Above all, taking the shield of faith, wherewith ye shall be able to quench all the fiery darts of the wicked.

And take the helmet of salvation, and the sword of the Spirit, which is the Word of God:

Praying always with all prayer and supplications in the Spirit, and watching thereunto with all perseverance and supplication for all saints.

325 REASONABLE SERVICE
Romans 12:1-13

I beseech you therefore, brethren, by the mercies of God, to present your bodies a living sacrifice, holy, acceptable to God, which is your reasonable service.

And be not conformed to this world; but be ye transformed by the renewing of your mind.

That ye may prove what is the good, and acceptable, and perfect will of God.

For I say, through the grace that was given me, to every man that is among you, not to think of himself more highly than he ought to think;

But to think soberly, according as God hath dealt to each man a measure of faith.

For even as we have many members in one body, and all the members have not the same office:

So we, who are many, are one body in Christ, and every one members one of another.

And having gifts differing according to the grace that was given to us,

Whether prophecy, let us prophesy according to the proportion of our faith;

Or ministry, let us give ourselves to our ministry;

Or he that teacheth, to his teaching;

Or he that exhorteth, to his exhorting;

He that giveth, let him do it with liberality;

He that ruleth, with diligence;

He that showeth mercy, with cheerfulness.

Let love be without dissimulation, abhor that which is evil; cleave to that which is good.

Be kindly affectioned one to another with brotherly love; in honor preferring one another;

Not slothful in business; fervent in spirit; serving the Lord;

Rejoicing in hope; patient in tribulation; continuing instant in prayer;

Distributing to the necessities of the saints; given to hospitality.

326 WISDOM AND UNDER-STANDING
Proverbs 3:13-23, 26

Happy is the man that findeth wisdom, and the man that getteth understanding:

For the merchandise of it is better than the merchandise of silver, and the gain thereof than fine gold.

She is more precious than rubies:

And none of the things thou canst desire are to be compared unto her.

Length of days is in her right hand; in her left hand are riches and honor.

Her ways are ways of pleasantness, and all her paths are peace.

She is a tree of life to them that lay hold upon her:

And happy is every one that retaineth her.

The Lord by wisdom hath founded the earth; by understanding hath he established the heavens.

By his knowledge the depths are broken up, and the clouds drop down the dew.

My son, let them not depart from thine eyes; keep sound wisdom and discretion:

So shall they be life unto thy soul, and grace to thy neck.

Then shalt thou walk in thy way safely, and thy foot shall not stumble.

For the Lord shall be thy confidence, and shall keep thy foot from being taken.

327 THE FORGIVING FATHER
Luke 15:11-24; 1 John 3:1

And he said, A certain man had two sons:

And the younger of them said to his father,

Father, give me the portion of goods that falleth to me. And he divided unto them his living.

And not many days after the younger son gathered all together, and took his journey into a far country, and there wasted his substance with riotous living.

And when he had spent all, there arose a mighty famine in that land; and he began to be in want.

And he went and joined himself to a citizen of that country; and he sent him into his fields to feed swine.

And he would fain have filled his belly with the husks that the swine did eat; and no man gave unto him.

And when he came to himself, he said, How many hired servants of my father's have bread enough and to spare, and I perish with hunger!

I will arise and go to my father, and will say unto him, Father, I have sinned against heaven, and before thee,

And am no more worthy to be called thy son: make me as one of thy hired servants.

And he arose and came to his father.

But when he was yet a great way off, his father saw him, and had compassion, and ran, and fell on his neck, and kissed him.

And the son said unto him,

Father, I have sinned against heaven, and in thy sight, and am no more worthy to be called thy son.

But the father said to his servants, Bring forth the best robe and put it on him; and put a ring on his hand, and shoes on his feet:

And bring hither the fatted calf, and kill it; and let us eat and be merry;

For this my son was dead, and is alive again; he was lost, and is found.

Behold, what manner of love the Father hath bestowed upon us, that we should be called the sons of God.

328 THE LAW OF THE LORD
Psalm 19:7-11; 119:9-16; 19:14

The law of the Lord is perfect, converting the soul: the testimony of the Lord is sure, making wise the simple:

The statutes of the Lord are right, rejoicing the heart: the commandment of the Lord is pure, enlightening the eyes:

The fear of the Lord is clean, enduring for ever: the judgments of the Lord are true and righteous altogether.

More to be desired are they than gold, yea, than much fine gold; sweeter also than honey, and the honey-comb.

Moreover by them is thy servant warned: and in keeping of them there is great reward.

Wherewithal shall a young man cleanse his way? By taking heed thereto according to thy word.

With my whole heart have I sought thee: O let me not wander from thy commandments.

Thy word have I hid in mine heart, that I might not sin against thee.

Blessed art thou, O Lord: teach me thy statutes.

With my lips have I declared all the judgments of thy mouth.

I have rejoiced in the way of thy testimonies, as much as in all riches.

I will meditate in thy precepts, and have respect unto thy ways.

I will delight myself in thy statutes: I will not forget thy word.

Let the words of my mouth, and the meditation of my heart, be acceptable in thy sight, O Lord, my strength, and my redeemer.

TOPICAL INDEX

TOPICAL INDEX

GENERAL INDEX

INDEX

RAINBOW LITHOGRAPHING CO.
MUSIC PRINTERS · CHICAGO, ILL.